Supreme Court Case Studies

McGraw-Hill

New York, New York   Columbus, Ohio   Mission Hills, California   Peoria, Illinois

TO THE TEACHER

This resource booklet contains 66 reproducible Supreme Court case studies to accompany Glencoe Social Studies products. These cases include landmark decisions in American government that have helped and continue to shape this nation, as well as decisions dealing with current issues in American society. Every case includes background information, the constitutional issue under consideration, the court's decision, and where appropriate, dissenting opinions.

Each two-page study requires students to analyze the case and apply critical thinking skills. An answer key is provided in the back of the booklet.

Creating a Customized File

There are numerous ways to organize the Glencoe Social Studies teaching aids. Several alternatives are given below.

- Organize by category (all activities, all tests, etc.)

- Organize by category and chapter (all chapter 1 activities, all chapter 1 tests, etc.)

- Organize sequentially by lesson (activities, quizzes, and other materials for Section 1, Section 2, etc.)

No matter what organization you use, you can pull out individual worksheets from these booklets, or you may photocopy directly from the booklet and file the photocopies. You will then be able to keep original booklets intact and in a safe place.

Glencoe/McGraw-Hill

A Division of The McGraw·Hill Companies

Send all inquiries to:
Glencoe/McGraw-Hill
936 Eastwind Drive
Westerville, Ohio 43081-3374

Printed in the United States of America

1 2 3 4 5 6 7 8 9 10 024 02 01 00 99 98 97

SUPREME COURT CASE STUDIES

TABLE OF CONTENTS

SUPREME COURT CASE   1

MARBURY V. MADISON (1803)

Background of the Case

The election of 1800 transferred power from the Federalist party to the Republican party. In the closing days of President John Adams' administration, the Federalists created many new offices, appointing Federalists to fill them. One of these last-minute appointments was William Marbury, who was appointed as a justice of the peace for the District of Columbia. His commission papers had been signed and sealed, but Adams' acting secretary of state, John Marshall, somehow neglected to deliver these papers.

After taking office, President Thomas Jefferson ordered his new secretary of state, James Madison, not to deliver the commission papers. Marbury then applied to the Supreme Court for a writ of *mandamus,* or an order from a court that some action be performed, commanding that Madison deliver the commission. Such writs had been authorized by the Judiciary Act of 1789.

Constitutional Issues

In 1803, John Marshall, now Chief Justice, reviewed the case on the basis of three questions: (1) Did Marbury have a right to the commission? (2) If so, was he entitled to some remedy under United States law? (3) Was that remedy a writ from a Supreme Court? Marshall's answers led to the Court's first declaration holding an act of Congress unconstitutional. This decision established the principle of judicial review.

The Court's Decision

Justice Marshall decided the first question by holding that an appointment is effective once a commission has been signed and the U.S. seal affixed. Therefore, Marbury had been legally appointed, and Madison's refusal to deliver the commission violated Marbury's right to the appointment. A long-established legal principle states that where a right exists, a corresponding remedy for any violation of that right must exist as well. Accordingly, in response to his second question, Marshall held that Marbury was entitled to some remedy under United States law.

The final question dealt with whether the proper remedy for Marbury was applying for a writ against Madison and whether the Supreme Court was empowered to issue such a writ.

Considering the Constitutional separation of powers, Marshall reasoned that there is a difference between a cabinet secretary acting according to the President's orders and acting as directed by law. The former would improperly involve the Court in a political area. The latter, however, involves legal questions that are properly part of the Court's business.

Since Marbury had no other course of legal action open to him, and since Madison could properly be served with a writ to comply with the law, Marshall ruled that Marbury did indeed have a right to this specific remedy under U.S. law.

Finally, Marshall examined whether the Supreme Court had the power to issue the writ, saying that "if this court is not authorized to issue a writ of *mandamus* . . . it must be because the law is unconstitutional."

According to Article III of the Constitution, the Supreme Court has the duty to hear certain cases directly (original jurisdiction). In all other instances, it hears cases only on appeal (appellate jurisdiction). The Court had not been given the authority of original jurisdiction necessary to issue a writ of *mandamus* by the Constitution, and Marshall held that the Constitution gives Congress no power to add new instances of original jurisdiction.

Nonetheless, Congress had in fact passed such a law. Should the Court enforce it? Marshall said that it should not because the law was unconstitutional, and therefore, void. The sole remaining issue, then, was to decide who was responsible for determining that a law was unconstitutional. In Marshall's opinion, "It is emphatically the province and duty of the judicial department to say what the law is. . . . If two laws conflict with each other, the courts must decide on the operation of each." Thus Marshall declared the Supreme Court as the final judge of constitutionality.

Contemporary observers, however, were much more interested in the practical result of the ruling—that the Court could not issue the writ, and that it therefore could not attempt to force the appointment of Marbury. By the time the Court next declared a law unconstitutional, more than 50 years had passed and by then the idea of judicial review had become a time-honored principle.

Analyzing the Case

1. What legal principle gave Marbury a right to some remedy under law?

_____

_____

_____

2. Why was Marshall hesitant to serve a cabinet officer with a writ?

_____

_____

_____

3. Why is *Marbury* v. *Madison* of particular importance to the role of the Court?

_____

_____

_____

Critical Thinking

4. **Determining Relevance** In what way does *Marbury* enhance the system of checks and balances?

_____

_____

_____

_____

_____

_____

_____

_____

_____

SUPREME COURT CASE 2

MCCULLOCH V. MARYLAND (1819)

Background of the Case

The Supreme Court was first called on to "umpire" a dispute between a national and a state law in 1819. The Second Bank of the United States had been chartered by Congress in 1816. The tight credit policies of the bank contributed to a depression and caused many states to react against what they saw as "the monster monopoly." Two states prohibited the bank from operating within their jurisdiction. Six other states taxed bank operations within their jurisdictions. In 1818 the Maryland legislature passed a law that would have placed a substantial tax on the operations of the Baltimore branch of the bank. James McCulloch, the bank's cashier, issued bank notes without paying the tax that the Maryland law now required. After Maryland state courts ruled against McCulloch, he appealed to the United States Supreme Court.

Constitutional Issue

The Constitutional questions in the *McCulloch* case concern both the powers of Congress and the relationship between federal and state authorities. Does the Constitution permit Congress to charter a bank? Does a state have the power to tax a corporation established by the federal government? The resolution of the *McCulloch* case focused on the meaning of the "necessary and proper" clause of Article I, Section 8, of the United States Constitution.

The Court's Decision

Chief Justice John Marshall wrote the decision for a unanimous Court. He started with the question, "Has Congress power to incorporate a bank?"

In first determining the extent of Congressional power, Marshall held that the Constitution is a creation not of the states, but of the people, acting through statewide constitutional conventions. Therefore, the states are bound in obligation to the Constitution, which is "the supreme law of the land." Justice Marshall summed up the decision based on the Supremacy Clause saying, "If any one proposition could command the universal assent of mankind we might expect it to be this—that the government of the Union, though limited in its powers, is supreme within its sphere of action. . . . The states have no power to retard, impede, burden, or in any manner control, the operation of the constitutional laws enacted by Congress."

Although the specific powers of Congress do not include the power to charter a corporation, the section enumerating these powers includes a statement giving Congress the authority to make all laws "necessary and proper" for executing its specified tasks. In Marshall's analysis, the terms "necessary and proper" grant Congress "an additional power, not a restriction on those already granted." This conclusion led Marshall to state the doctrine of *implied powers*—powers necessary to carry out specified granted powers. "Let the end be legitimate, let it be within the scope of the Constitution, and all means which are appropriate, which are plainly adapted to that end, which are not prohibited, but consistent with the letter and spirit of the Constitution, are constitutional," the Chief Justice wrote. Therefore, Marshall determined, the choice of means is for Congress to decide. In the *McCulloch* case, the Court held that Congress had the power to incorporate a bank.

On the question of the validity of Maryland's bank tax, Marshall again noted the Constitution's supremacy, but he also recognized a state's constitutional right to impose taxes. Echoing his earlier argument, Marshall observed that a government may properly tax its subjects or their property.

However, the federal government and its agencies are not subjects of any state. A tax on a national institution by one state would be an indirect tax on citizens in other states, who would not benefit from such a tax.

Furthermore, the power to tax, if misused, is also the power to destroy or harm an institution. The power of Congress to establish an institution must imply the right to take all steps necessary for its preservation. In a conflict between the federal power to create and preserve a corporation and a state's power to levy a tax, the state must yield, the Court decided. Therefore, it denied Maryland's power to tax the operations of the Second Bank of the United States. In this way Marshall ensured the power of Congress to enact legislation under "a Constitution intended to endure for ages to come, and, consequently, to be adapted to the various *crises* of human affairs."

Analyzing the Case

1. What are implied powers?

_____

_____

_____

_____

2. What is the objective of the "necessary and proper" clause?

_____

_____

_____

3. Why did the Court decide that the Second Bank of the United States was immune from taxation?

_____

_____

_____

Critical Thinking

4. **Drawing Conclusions** How did the ruling in *McCulloch* v. *Maryland* contribute to strengthening the national government?

_____

_____

_____

_____

_____

_____

_____

SUPREME COURT CASE   3

GIBBONS V. OGDEN (1824)

Background of the Case

Robert Fulton, the inventor of the steamboat, had had a 20-year monopoly granted him by the New York State Legislature for steamboat navigation in New York. The original grant was given in 1798 on the understanding that within one year he would build a steamboat capable of going at four miles per hour against the current on the Hudson River. His project was plagued by delays, however, and six times he had to return to the legislature in order to get an extension, much to everyone's amusement. Finally in 1807 "Fulton's Folly," as it had been dubbed, was a success.

In 1811 Fulton's company assigned Ogden a license to run a ferry service on the Hudson between New York and New Jersey—a very profitable business. Seeking to take advantage of this, Gibbons secured a license from the federal government to engage in the coastal trade, and started up a competing New York-New Jersey ferry service.

Claiming that his monopoly rights were being infringed, Ogden sought and obtained an injunction in a New York State court forbidding Gibbons' ferry from docking in New York. After obtaining the services of Daniel Webster as his lawyer, Gibbons appealed to the United States Supreme Court.

Constitutional Issue

Three major constitutional issues were raised. The first two fell under the Commerce Clause of Article I, Section 8, which gave Congress the power "to regulate commerce with foreign nations, and among the several States, and with the Indian tribes." The precise questions were whether navigation should be understood to be a part of commerce and, if so, to what extent might Congress regulate it. The third question was whether Congress in fact had an exclusive right to regulate interstate commerce. This question, however, was not fully resolved in this case.

The Court's Decision

The Court held in Gibbons' favor. Chief Justice John Marshall wrote this landmark decision.

Ogden had argued that commerce did not include navigation, but was limited "to traffic, to buying and selling, or to the exchange of commodities. . . ." Marshall agreed that this was one of its meanings, but that it was still "something more." Specifically, "It describes the commercial intercourse between nations, and parts of nations, in all its branches, and is regulated by prescribing rules for carrying on that intercourse. The mind can scarcely conceive a system for regulating commerce between nations which shall exclude navigation. . . ." The same reasoning must apply to commerce between states and, in fact, the United States government had always regulated navigation. "All America understands, and has uniformly understood the word 'commerce' to comprehend navigation." Thus the Court held that "a power to regulate navigation is as expressly granted as if that term had been added to the word 'commerce.'"

That settled, Marshall now turned to the meaning of "among," as in "among the several states." He reasoned that since "among" means "intermingle with," "Commerce among the states cannot stop at the external boundary line of each state but may be introduced into the interior." Congress had no power over commerce which is confined to one state alone, but that power was in full force as soon as a state's boundary line had been crossed. And the power to regulate must necessarily follow any commerce in question right across those boundaries; otherwise the power would be "useless."

Having established that Congress has a regulatory power over commerce which includes navigation and crosses state lines, the Court turned to the question of the extent of such power. Its conclusion was that it is, like other congressional powers, unlimited so long as it is applied to objects specified in the Constitution. Commerce is such an object, and the Constitution places no limit on Congress's power to regulate it.

This immediately raised the further question as to whether Congress's power is then exclusive, preventing a state from making its own regulations in this area. The Chief Justice cited Webster's argument that full power to regulate necessarily excludes others from performing "the same operation on the same thing." Marshall declined to fully endorse this line of reasoning, saying, "There is great force in this argument, and the Court is not satisfied that it has been refuted."

Instead, Marshall observed simply that there was a conflict here between New York's law and a federal statute. "In every such case, the act of Congress . . . is supreme; and the law of the state . . . must yield to it." Gibbons' right to operate ferry service in competition with Ogden was therefore upheld.

Analyzing the Case

1. Under what authority did Gibbons and Ogden operate their ferry services?

_____

_____

_____

2. How does Congress get its power to regulate commerce within a state?

_____

_____

_____

Critical Thinking

3. **Identifying Central Issues** What was the Court's decision as to whether Congress's power to regulate interstate commerce excluded similar state regulation?

_____

_____

_____

_____

_____

_____

_____

_____

_____

SUPREME COURT CASE   4

DRED SCOTT V. SANFORD (1857)

Background of the Case

Dred Scott was a slave owned by John Emerson, a U.S. Army surgeon stationed in Missouri. Dr. Emerson took Scott to Illinois, which was a free state in 1834. They moved to the territory of Upper Louisiana (now Minnesota), where slavery had been forbidden under the terms of the Missouri Compromise. In 1838, Emerson and Scott returned to Missouri.

In 1846, Scott won a suit in a Missouri state court, based on his claim that by living in free territory, he had earned his freedom. That ruling was overturned, however, by Missouri's Supreme Court.

Various anti-slavery interests now arranged a fictitious sale of Scott to John Sanford of New York, Emerson's brother-in-law. This action classified the issue as a dispute between citizens of different states. Therefore, it now came under the jurisdiction of the federal court system.

The federal court held that Scott still was a slave and Sanford's property. Scott then appealed to the United States Supreme Court on a writ of error—a claim that a mistake had been made in legal interpretation.

Constitutional Issue

The first major issue of the case was whether Scott qualified as a citizen of the United States, who would then be entitled to sue in a federal court. Although the Constitution does not say what makes a United States citizen, and no simple test has ever been devised, some states have at times allowed resident aliens to vote.

The second issue concerned whether Scott had gained his freedom by moving to a free territory or state. Which laws would govern his status: those of Missouri, Illinois, or those of the territory?

The third issue focused on the Missouri Compromise of 1820. Did Congress have the power to prohibit slavery in the territories, and to make the prohibition a condition of admission to the Union?

The Court's Decision

The *Dred Scott* decision contains eight separate opinions and comprises more than 200 pages. Here, discussion is limited to Chief Justice Roger B. Taney's opinion and Justice Benjamin R. Curtis' dissent.

Chief Justice Taney began the decision written for the Court with a discussion of citizenship. His first and most notorious ruling was that African Americans, "whether emancipated or not," did not qualify as United States citizens. Taney explained that only those who were state citizens when the Union was formed became federal citizens; slaves and their descendants were not and are not citizens. And even though a state may emancipate a slave, give him the right to vote, and admit him to state citizenship, none of these actions would automatically give him federal citizenship. The right to grant federal citizenship belonged exclusively to Congress. Given this reasoning, Taney concluded, Scott was not and never had become a citizen of the United States. Therefore, he was not entitled to sue in a federal court.

Taney next examined the question of whether Scott had gained his freedom when he entered the Upper Louisiana Territory. The Chief Justice attacked the Missouri Compromise as an unconstitutional exercise of congressional authority. A territory becomes a state like any other state, possessing all powers guaranteed it by the Constitution, Taney stated. Congress cannot therefore forbid a state from making slavery legal. Taney explained that so long as slavery is authorized by the Constitution, Congress cannot alter the right of a person to own slaves or any other kind of property. In viewing the Compromise as unconstitutional, the Court determined that Scott's status had not changed from slave to freeman by entering the Louisiana Territory. The Court also found that Scott had been held in Illinois as a slave and had returned to Missouri as a slave. On his return to Missouri he became subject to Missouri law alone. Given, then, that Scott was not a citizen of Missouri, Taney ordered the suit dismissed for lack of jurisdiction.

A Dissenting Opinion

Justice Curtis wrote a dissenting opinion, which focused primarily on citizenship for free-born African Americans. In Taney's opinion, African Americans were ineligible for citizenship in the slave states and they were also ineligible for citizenship in the United States. Curtis noted that, however, African Americans were among those who originally ratified the Constitution in a number of states. Nothing in the Constitution stripped these free African Americans of their citizenship. Curtis maintained that "under the Constitution of the United States, every free person born on the soil of a State, who is a citizen of that State by force of its Constitution or laws, is also a citizen of the United States. . . ."

Analyzing the Case

1. Why did Dred Scott claim that he became a freeman by entering the Louisiana Territory?

_____

_____

_____

2. On what basis did the Court rule that Scott was not a citizen?

_____

_____

_____

Critical Thinking

3. **Drawing Conclusions** What was unconstitutional about the Missouri Compromise? What relationship did this unconstitutional compromise have to Dred Scott's citizenship?

_____

_____

_____

_____

_____

_____

_____

_____

_____

_____

SUPREME COURT CASE 5

EX PARTE MILLIGAN (1866)

Background of the Case

In 1864, during the Civil War, Lambdin P. Milligan, a civilian resident of Indiana, was arrested by order of General Hovey who commanded the military district of Indiana. Milligan was charged and tried before a military tribunal for his part in a plot to free Confederate war prisoners and overthrow three state governments. He had been tried by military courts, although state courts in Indiana were still functioning. The military court found him guilty, and Milligan was sentenced to death by hanging. This sentence was approved by President Johnson.

On May 10, 1865, Milligan petitioned the Circuit Court of Indiana for a writ of *habeas corpus* on grounds of unlawful imprisonment. He claimed that the proceedings of his conviction were unconstitutional and that he was denied the right of a trial by jury. As a citizen of Indiana who was not in the military, Milligan claimed he should not have been tried by a military court. The case was appealed to the United States Supreme Court. For the first time, the Supreme Court faced deciding the right of the President to suspend the writ of *habeas corpus* and to substitute the authority of a military court for that of a civilian court.

Constitutional Issue

Article I, Section 9, paragraph 2, of the Constitution provides that "the Privileges of the Writ of *Habeas Corpus* shall not be suspended, unless when in Cases of Rebellion or Invasion the public Safety may require it." The questions at issue were whether Congress had the power to suspend the writ of *habeas corpus* and whether civilians may become subject to military law.

The Court's Decision

Justice David Davis, writing for a 5 to 4 majority, declared the military's assumed authority invalid. He said that "The Constitution is a law for rulers and people, equally in war and in peace." Further stating the enormity of the matter being considered, "No graver question was ever considered by this Court, nor one which more nearly concerns the rights of the whole people: for it is the birthright of every American citizen when charged with a crime, to be tried and punished according to law. . . . By the protection of the law human rights are secured; withdraw that protection, and they are at the mercy of wicked rulers, or the clamor of an excited people. If there was law to justify this military trial, it is not our province to interfere; if there was not, it is our duty to declare the nullity of the whole proceedings."

As stated, the Court did nullify the finding of the military court. Congress had not granted to the nation's military courts the power to try civilians, and indeed could not do so, especially so long as civilian courts were still operating. "One of the plainest constitutional provisions was, therefore, infringed when Milligan was tried by a court not ordained and established by Congress. . . ." Such action, the Court ruled, "destroys every guarantee of the Constitution, and effectively renders the 'military independent of and superior to the civil power.'"

Davis agreed that "in a great crisis . . . there should be a power somewhere of suspending the writ of *habeas corpus.*" However, in this case, such power was to be exercised by the judicial branch. Davis declared that the writ itself may not be suspended, but rather the privilege the writ would grant. A court must decide whether the privilege is to be denied in a particular instance.

Davis recognized that there may be circumstances in which the courts might be closed and civil authority overthrown, thus making necessary government by martial law. Even then, military rule would be strictly limited to the place where the crisis occurred and last only for the duration of that crisis. In any case, such military rule cannot be imposed while the civil authority still operates.

In relation to martial law in this case, Davis wrote, "It is difficult to see how the safety of the country required martial law in Indiana. If any of her citizens were plotting treason, the power of [civil] arrest could secure them, until the government was prepared for their trial, when the courts were open and ready to try them. It was as easy to protect witnesses before a civil as well as a military tribunal; and as there could be no wish to convict, except on sufficient legal evidence, surely an ordained and established court were better able to judge of this than a military tribunal composed of gentlemen not trained to the profession of the law."

As a point of interest, Milligan's death sentence had been commuted to life imprisonment by the President in June 1865. He was released in April 1866 as a result of the Supreme Court decision. He then sued General Hovey for unlawful imprisonment and won his case, although damages awarded were minimal because of a two-year statute of limitations that only allowed him to recover damages for about a month of his imprisonment.

Analyzing the Case

1. What position did Justice Davis take concerning the use of military or martial law?

_____

_____

_____

2. How did the military infringe on Milligan's rights?

_____

_____

_____

Critical Thinking

3. **Understanding Cause and Effect** Describe a situation in which military rule would take precedence over civilian authority.

_____

_____

_____

_____

_____

_____

_____

_____

_____

_____

SUPREME COURT CASE   6

REYNOLDS V. UNITED STATES (1879)

Background of the Case

George Reynolds was a member of the Church of Jesus Christ of Latter Day Saints, also known as the Mormons. The Mormons believed in the religious duty of males, circumstances permitting, to practice polygamy, or multiple marriages. Reynolds had followed that teaching and found himself indicted for bigamy—having more than one legal wife—under the federal statutes governing the territory which was then Utah. He was sentenced to a term of imprisonment at hard labor. Reynolds appealed this decision to the United States Supreme Court.

Constitutional Issue

The constitutional issue in this case focused on whether the federal anti-bigamy statute conflicted with that clause of the First Amendment guaranteeing the free exercise of religion.

The Court's Decision

The Court ruled unanimously that Reynolds' conviction was constitutional. However, the Court subsequently held that punishment under the anti-bigamy statute could not include hard labor.

Chief Justice Morrison R. Waite wrote for the Court. Waite agreed that "Congress cannot pass a law for the government of the Territories which shall prohibit the free exercise of religion." The question was whether the law violated this prohibition. Waite stated, "The precise point is, What is the religious freedom which has been guaranteed?"

Waite undertook a historical analysis of religion and religious freedom from the late 1600s through to the 1780s and ratification of the Constitution. He concluded that "Congress was deprived of all legislative power over mere opinion, but was left free to reach actions which were in violation of social duties or subversive of good order."

He reviewed the history of laws in England and elsewhere regarding polygamy. Waite found that "polygamy has always been odious among the Northern and Western Nations of Europe and, until the establishment of the Mormon Church, was almost exclusively a feature of the life of Asiatic and African people." He wrote, "We think it may safely be said there never has been a time in any State of the Union when polygamy has not been an offense against society, cognizable [recognized] by the civil courts and punishable with more or less severity. In the face of all this evidence, it is impossible to believe that the constitutional guarantee of religious freedom was intended to prohibit legislation in respect to this most important feature of social life."

Regarding marriage, Waite wrote, "Marriage, while from its very nature a sacred obligation, is, nevertheless, in most civilized nations, a civil contract, and usually regulated by law." With that being stated, Waite concluded, "In our opinion the statute immediately under consideration . . . is constitutional and valid . . . in all places over which the United States has control."

The anti-bigamy law was found valid. Then, it remained to determine whether the Mormons should be exempted on grounds of religious beliefs. Waite asked, "Suppose one believed that human sacrifices were a necessary part of religious worship. Would it seriously be contended that the civil government could not interfere . . . ?"

Waite continued, "So here, as a law of the organization of society under the exclusive dominion of the United States, it is provided that plural marriages shall not be allowed. Can a man excuse his practices to the contrary because of his religious belief? To permit this would be to make the professed doctrines of religious belief superior to the law of the land, and in effect to permit every citizen to become a law unto himself. Government could exist only in name under such circumstances." In this way, the Supreme Court determined that the freedom of religion, like other freedoms, has its constitutional limits. No freedom, based on the Constitution, is absolute.

Thus, the existing law was upheld regarding bigamy. It read, "Every person having a husband or wife living, who marries another, whether married or single, in a Territory, or other place over which the United States have exclusive jurisdiction, is guilty of bigamy, and shall be punished by a fine of not more than $500, and by imprisonment for a term of not more than five years."

Analyzing the Case

1. According to Waite, what authority did Congress have to regulate religious practice in the territories?

_____

_____

_____

2. Why could the First Amendment not protect the practice of polygamy?

_____

_____

_____

3. What precedent did the *Reynolds* case set?

_____

_____

_____

Critical Thinking

4. Demonstrating Reasoned Judgment Why do you think "freedom" in a democratic society must have limits?

_____

_____

_____

_____

_____

_____

_____

_____

_____

_____

SUPREME COURT CASE   7

PLESSY V. FERGUSON (1896)

Background of the Case

An 1890 Louisiana law commanded railroads to "provide equal but separate accommodations for the white and colored races." The law went on to state, "No person or persons shall be permitted to occupy seats in coaches, other than the ones assigned to them, on account of the race they belong to . . . and should any passenger refuse to occupy the coach or compartment to which he or she is assigned, by the officer of such railway, said officer shall have the power to refuse to carry such passenger on his train, and for such refusal neither he nor the railway company which he represents shall be liable for damages in any of the courts in this state." Violation of this law carried a fine of $20 or 25 days in jail. Railway personnel were responsible for assigning seats according to race.

On June 7, 1892, Plessy, who was one-eighth African American, attempted to sit in the white section of a train going from New Orleans to Covington, Louisiana. He had paid for a first-class passage. When a conductor ordered Plessy to give up his seat, he refused. He was forcibly ejected from the train with the aid of a police officer. He was then arrested and ordered imprisoned in the parish jail of New Orleans by Ferguson, a local judge. He went before the district court and was found guilty. On appeal, the Louisiana Supreme Court found that the statute under which Plessy had been arrested was valid.

Constitutional Issue

Plessy appealed to the United States Supreme Court on the grounds that Louisiana's statute violated the Thirteenth Amendment, which forbids slavery, and the Fourteenth Amendment, which prohibits the states from denying "to any person within its jurisdiction the equal protection of the law."

The Court's Decision

Justice Henry Brown wrote for a seven-member majority, with Justice John Harlan dissenting (one justice was absent). The issue related to the Thirteenth Amendment was quickly brushed aside. The Court held that "a legal distinction between the white and colored races . . . has no tendency to destroy the legal equality of the two races."

However, concerned with the Fourteenth Amendment, Brown concluded that it aimed strictly "to enforce the absolute equality of the two races before the law," but that it "could not have been intended to abolish distinctions based on color, or to enforce social, as distinguished from political, equality. . . ." Laws requiring segregation "do not necessarily imply the inferiority of either race to the other . . . ," he stated. Brown called this "the underlying fallacy" of Plessy's case and postulated that an African American-controlled legislature might someday enact similar laws, which would also be valid under the Fourteenth Amendment.

The Court ruled, then, that the matter ultimately depends on whether Louisiana's statute was "reasonable." The majority opinion explained that segregation laws "have been generally, if not universally, recognized as within the competency of the state legislatures in the exercise of their police power." In such matters, a legislature is free to take into account "established usages, customs, and traditions of the people," as well as "the preservation of public peace and good order."

Finally, Brown rejected the notion that "social prejudices may be overcome by legislation." He maintained, "If the civil and political rights of both races be equal, one cannot be inferior to the other civilly or politically. If one race be inferior to the other socially, the Constitution of the United States cannot put them on the same plane."

A Dissenting Opinion

Justice Harlan's dissent first criticized the majority opinion for ignoring the true intent of Louisiana's statute, which was "under the guise of giving equal accommodation for whites and blacks, to compel the latter to keep to themselves while travelling in railroad passenger coaches." Harlan's "fundamental objection" to the statute was that it "interferes with the personal freedom of citizens. No government should be able to infringe the right of one race to choose to travel with another."

Harlan saw segregation on racial lines as "a badge of servitude wholly inconsistent with the civil freedom and equality before the law established by the Constitution. . . . The thin disguise of 'equal' accommodations for passengers in railroad coaches will not mislead anyone, nor atone for the wrong this day done."

Analyzing the Case

1. What was the basis of Plessy's appeal?

_____

_____

_____

2. What reasoning does Justice Brown label as a "fallacy"?

_____

_____

_____

3. How does Justice Brown view the Fourteenth Amendment?

_____

_____

_____

Critical Thinking

4. Identifying Central Issues What conclusion does Justice Harlan come to in his dissent about racial separation and personal freedom?

_____

_____

_____

_____

_____

_____

_____

_____

_____

SUPREME COURT CASE 8

WEEKS V. UNITED STATES (1914)

Background of the Case

Weeks was arrested at his place of business on a charge of sending lottery tickets through the mail. The police turned over various papers found there to a United States marshall. The marshall, in turn, searched Weeks' premises in the company of police officers and took still other papers. No warrants had ever been issued for any of the searches or for Weeks' arrest.

Prior to trial, Weeks requested the return of his papers. This request was denied. Those documents were used in evidence against him at his trial and Weeks was indicted. The Supreme Court agreed to review Weeks' case.

Constitutional Issue

The constitutional issue concerned the Fourth Amendment, which promises that "the right of the people to be secure in their persons, houses, papers, and effects against unreasonable searches and seizures, shall not be violated, and no warrants shall issue, but upon probable cause, . . . and particularly describing the place to be searched, and the persons or things to be seized."

The Court's Decision

The Court decided that Weeks' Fourth Amendment rights had indeed been violated. Justice William R. Day wrote for the Court.

Common law had long held that illegally seized evidence may still be admitted as evidence at a trial. The source of the evidence was held to be of no direct concern to the court; if it had been taken illegally or stolen, the remedy was to be found in a subsequent civil suit for trespass or in criminal prosecution for theft. In *Boyd* v. *United States* (1886) the Court implicitly reversed this common law principle, but it was not until *Weeks* that the Exclusionary Rule, as it came to be called, became a definite legal standard. This new rule meant that illegally seized evidence would be excluded from a criminal trial.

Day wrote, "The tendency of those who execute the criminal laws of this country to obtain conviction by means of unlawful seizures and enforced confessions, the latter often obtained after subjecting accused persons to unwarranted practices destructive of rights secured by the federal Constitution, should find no sanction in the judgments of the courts, which are charged at all times with the support of the Constitution, and to which people of all conditions have a right to appeal for the maintenance of such fundamental rights. . . ."

He continued, "If letters and private documents can thus be seized and held and used as evidence against a citizen accused of an offense, the protection of the Fourth Amendment, declaring his right to be secure against such searches and seizures, is of no value, and, so far as those thus placed are concerned, might as well be stricken from the Constitution. The efforts of the courts and their officials to bring the guilty to punishment, praiseworthy as they are, are not to be aided by the sacrifice of those great principles established by years of endeavor and suffering which have resulted in their embodiment in the fundamental law of the land."

Day wrote further, "We therefore reach the conclusion that the letters in question were taken from the house of the accused by an official of the United States, acting under color of his office in direct violation of the constitutional rights of the defendant; that having made a reasonable application for their return, which was heard and passed upon by the court, there was involved in the order refusing the application a denial of the constitutional rights of the accused, and that the court should have restored these letters to the accused. In holding them and permitting their use upon the trial, we think prejudicial error was committed.

"As to the papers and property seized by the policemen, it does not appear that they acted under any claim of federal authority such as would make the amendment applicable to such unauthorized seizures. The record shows that what they did by way of arrest and search and seizure was done before the finding of the indictment in the Federal court; under what supposed right or authority does not appear. What remedies the defendant may have against them we need not inquire, as the Fourth Amendment is not directed to individual misconduct of such officials. Its limitations reach the Federal government and its agencies." Thus, this ruling was held to be applicable only in federal courts and/or against federal authorities.

The Exclusionary Rule arising from this case became an important standard in search and seizure cases. In summary, under the Fourth Amendment, any evidence obtained through unlawful seizure was excluded from federal trials. *Weeks* held that if such evidence were to be admitted at trial, the courts would become as guilty as the police who seized the evidence, and the integrity of the entire judicial process would be threatened.

Analyzing the Case

1. What does the Fourth Amendment require of a warrant?

_____

_____

_____

2. To whom did the *Weeks* ruling apply?

_____

_____

_____

Critical Thinking

3. **Analyzing Information** What was the common law position on illegally obtained evidence? How was it applied in the *Weeks* case?

_____

_____

_____

_____

_____

_____

_____

_____

_____

SUPREME COURT CASE 9

GITLOW V. NEW YORK (1925)

Background of the Case

Benjamin Gitlow was indicted and convicted for violating the 1902 New York Criminal Anarchy Act. The Act defined criminal anarchy as "the doctrine that organized government should be overthrown by force or violence, or by assassination of the executive head or any of the executive officials of government, or by any unlawful means." The prohibition applied to speaking, teaching, advising, printing, publishing, circulating, selling, distributing, or publicly displaying such doctrine.

Gitlow had been charged with teaching the necessity and duty to overthrow the government in two publications based largely on Marx and Engels' *Communist Manifesto*. The publications advocated "mass industrial revolts," which would develop into "mass political strikes and revolutionary mass action for the annihilation of the parliamentary state. . . ."

Constitutional Issue

At issue was whether the First Amendment's protections of press and speech were included or incorporated under the due process clause of the Fourteenth Amendment, thus making them applicable to the states. More specifically, was "subversive speech" protected from government regulation, control, or punishment?

The Court's Decision

The Court voted 7 to 2 to uphold Gitlow's conviction. Justice Edward Sanford wrote for the Court.

The more general claim, that the states were bound by the First Amendment through the due process clause, was handled almost in passing. Sanford explained, "For present purposes we may and do assume that freedom of speech and of the press . . . are among the fundamental personal rights and liberties protected by the due process clause of the Fourteenth Amendment from impairment by the states. . . ."

In an earlier case, *Schenck* v. *United States* (1919), Justice Oliver Wendell Holmes had formulated the "clear and present danger" test for questionable speech. Holmes maintained, "The question in every case is whether the words used are used in such circumstances and are of such a nature as to create a clear and present danger that they will bring about the substantive evils that Congress has a right to prevent."

The "right" of Congress or the states to censor is their "primary and essential right of self-preservation." Therefore, "a state may punish utterances endangering the foundations of organized government and threatening its overthrow by unlawful means. These imperil its own existence as a constitutional state."

Thus, as a legitimate exercise of its police power, wrote Sanford, a state may penalize "utterances advocating the overthrow of organized government by force, violence, and unlawful means" which are "inimical to the general welfare and involve . . . danger of substantive evil."

The Court further ruled that the state was not required to prove in each case that there was any particular likelihood that a given utterance would in fact bring any result. The Court held that the entire class of subversive speech, constitutionally, may be controlled by a statute.

The Preferred Freedoms doctrine that became central to the speech cases of the next few decades was aimed at undermining the *Gitlow* decision. In the 1950s, however, there was a return to *Gitlow* relative to the decisions in *Dennis* v. *United States* and *Yates* v. *United States*, both decided in 1951.

A Dissenting Opinion

Justice Holmes, who had written the opinion in *Schenck*, dissented in *Gitlow* on the ground that "it is manifest that there was no present danger of an attempt to overthrow the government by force on the part of the admittedly small minority who shared the defendant's views." Since no actual danger had been shown, only that subversive ideas had been published, Holmes thought Gitlow's conviction should be reversed.

Holmes concluded: "Every idea is an incitement. It offers itself for belief, and, if believed, it is acted on unless some other belief outweighs it. . . . The only difference between the expression of an opinion and an incitement in the narrower sense is the speaker's enthusiasm for the result. . . . If, in the long run, the beliefs expressed in proletarian dictatorship are destined to be accepted by the dominant forces of the community, the only meaning of free speech is that they should be given their chance and have their way."

Analyzing the Case

1. What is criminal anarchy?

_____

_____

_____

2. How did the Court defend the application of the First Amendment to the states?

_____

_____

_____

3. Was the state of New York required to prove that Gitlow's publications constituted an actual danger?

_____

_____

_____

Critical Thinking

4. **Demonstrating Reasoned Judgment** Do you agree with the decision of the Court? Explain your answer.

_____

_____

_____

_____

_____

_____

_____

_____

SUPREME COURT CASE   10

OLMSTEAD V. UNITED STATES (1928)

Background of the Case

Roy Olmstead was an importer and supplier of alcoholic beverages. Using an investment of $21,000, he and his partners had built a thriving business in Washington state. They employed 50 people and owned two ocean-going ships and an extensive warehouse and distribution system. Gross sales approximated $2 million annually, a large sum in 1928.

Between 1919 and 1933, the United States was governed by the Eighteenth Amendment to the Constitution, which prohibited the manufacture, sale, or import of alcohol. Olmstead and his associates were prosecuted, tried, and convicted in federal court for conspiracy to violate the National Prohibition Act.

Much of the evidence at their trials was gathered by means of taps on the three telephone lines used by Olmstead's office. The taps were made from the basement of the building. Other taps were placed on home telephones. None of the taps had been placed as a result of physical trespass on any defendant's property.

Constitutional Issue

The Fourth and Fifth Amendments were called into question in the *Olmstead* case. The Fourth Amendment provides that "the right of the people to be secure in their persons, houses, papers, and effects, against unreasonable searches and seizures, shall not be violated. . . ." The Fifth Amendment protects a person, charged with a criminal offense, from being a witness against himself or herself. Did either of these amendments prohibit evidence obtained from these telephone taps?

The Court's Decision

The Court ruled 6 to 3 against Olmstead. Chief Justice William H. Taft delivered the opinion of the court.

The Court confined its examination to Fourth Amendment questions. If the Fourth Amendment could not be held to have been violated, since no one compelled the defendants to speak over phone lines, neither could the Fifth Amendment.

Taft's argument turned on the issue of whether a wiretap was the constitutional equivalent of forcible entry. If so, the evidence obtained would be inadmissible in federal courts in accord with previous decisions such as in *Weeks* v. *United States* (1914).

Taft held that the Fourth Amendment "shows that the search is to be of material things—the person, the house, his papers or his effects. The description of the warrant necessary to make the proceeding lawful is that it must specify the place to be searched and the person or *things* to be seized."

He rejected any analogy to sealed letters, which the Court had held to be protected by the Fourth Amendment. Taft explained in his decision that, "The United States takes no such care of telegraph or telephone messages as of mailed, sealed letters. The Amendment does not forbid what was done here. There was no searching. There was no seizure. The evidence was secured by the use of hearing and that only. There was no entry of the houses or offices of the defendants." He insisted that it was an unwarranted expansion of the Fourth Amendment to apply it to hearing or sight.

The Court held further that telephone lines were not protected by the Fourth Amendment, since they "are no part of his house or office, any more than are the high ways along which they are stretched. . . . The reasonable view is that one who installs . . . a telephone with connection wires intends to project his voice to those outside, and that the wires beyond his house and message passing over them are not within the protection of the Fourth Amendment."

Finally, Taft ruled that this holding was in accord with the generally accepted common law rule that "if the tendered evidence was pertinent, the method of obtaining it was unimportant." He concluded that "a standard which would forbid the reception of evidence if obtained by other than nice ethical conduct by government officials would make society suffer and give criminals greater immunity than has been known heretofore."

Although this decision was harshly criticized, it stood until overruled in *Katz* v. *United States* (1967).

A Dissenting Opinion

Justice L. Brandeis wrote the main dissent. He disagreed with the Supreme Court's very narrow view of the Fourteenth Amendment and felt that the Court's decision amounted to allowing criminal activity by the government. He warned, in his dissention, that the "progress of science in furnishing the government with means of espionage" called for allowing a more flexible reading of the Fourteenth Amendment to "protect the right of personal security."

Analyzing the Case

1. What was the purpose of the Eighteenth Amendment?

_____

_____

_____

2. Why did the Court think that the Fourth Amendment did not apply to wiretaps?

_____

_____

_____

Critical Thinking

3. **Demonstrating Reasoned Judgment** What was Taft's fear if this kind of evidence was made inadmissible? Do you think Taft's fear was justified?

_____

_____

_____

_____

_____

_____

_____

_____

_____

_____

_____

SUPREME COURT CASE 11

NEAR V. MINNESOTA (1931)

Background of the Case

A 1925 Minnesota law sought to prevent newspapers, magazines, and other publications from printing obscene, malicious, scandalous, and defamatory material. Either public prosecutors or private citizens could request a court to issue an injunction to shut down a publication as "a public nuisance." Disobedience was punishable by a fine or a jail term.

The Saturday Press, published by Near, had printed articles charging that various criminal activities in Minnesota were controlled by a Jewish gangster, and that the local mayor, chief of police, and county attorney were in league with gangsters. Using the 1925 statute, the county attorney obtained an injunction "perpetually" prohibiting Near from publishing any "malicious, scandalous or defamatory newspaper." Near appealed to the Minnesota Supreme Court and then to the United States Supreme Court.

Constitutional Issue

The Court had to decide whether Minnesota's statute violated the First Amendment's guarantee of freedom of the press, as applied to the states through the due process clause of the Fourteenth Amendment.

The Court's Decision

The Court voted 5 to 4 in Near's favor. Chief Justice Charles Evans Hughes presented the Court's opinion. Hughes called the Minnesota statute "unusual, if not unique." It pitted the undoubted liberty of the press against the "necessarily admitted" authority of the state "to promote the health, safety, morals and general welfare of its people." Both the state's authority and the liberty of the press have claims and limits that must be delineated.

Justice Hughes wrote: "If we cut through mere details of procedure, the operation and effect of the statute in substance is that public authorities may bring the owner or publisher of a newspaper . . . before a judge upon a charge . . . of publishing scandalous and defamatory matter . . . and unless the owner or publisher is able and disposed to bring competent evidence to satisfy the judge that the charges are true and are published with good motives and for justifiable ends, his newspaper or periodical is suppressed and further publication is made punishable as a contempt. This is of the essence of censorship." This is not to say, however, that no forms of censorship are to be permitted, Hughes stressed. There are "exceptional cases," such as in times of war, when it may be permitted. Similarly, he observed, "the primary requirements of decency may be enforced against obscene publications."

Hughes continued, "In the present case, we have no occasion to inquire as to the permissible scope of subsequent punishment: For whatever wrong the appellant has committed or may commit, by his publications, the state appropriately affords both public and private redress by its libel laws." Here he was making the point that if, in fact, the claims of the paper were proved to be libelous, another court case would be called for. The decision of the Court here was not in relation to whether the articles in question were true or false.

What is at issue is prior or previous restraint upon the press in nonexceptional cases. On that score, Hughes wrote, the "chief purpose" of the liberty of the press is "to prevent previous restraints upon publication." The Court concluded that this in no way places the press beyond the reach of legal action. That is, the press is generally to be held accountable after, not before, publication.

In summary, Hughes wrote, "For these reasons we hold the statute . . . to be an infringement of the liberty of the press guaranteed by the Fourteenth Amendment. We should add that this decision rests upon the operation and effect of the statute, without regard to the question of truth of the charges contained in the particular periodical. The fact that the public officers named in this case, and those associated with charges of official dereliction, may be deemed to be impeccable, cannot affect the conclusion that the statute imposes an unconstitutional restraint upon publication."

Near announced a new level of Supreme Court concern for freedom of speech. Prior censorship of the press was condemned. *Near* was the first Court decision adopting the Incorporation Doctrine and striking down a state law in its totality on free speech grounds.

Analyzing the Case

1. What are examples of times when previous restraint on the press is permitted?

_____

_____

_____

2. What is the primary purpose of the freedom of the press, according to Hughes?

_____

_____

_____

Critical Thinking

3. **Identifying Alternatives** What remedy exists for someone who feels he or she has been damaged by published material?

_____

_____

_____

_____

_____

_____

_____

_____

_____

_____

_____

_____

_____

SUPREME COURT CASE 12

POWELL V. ALABAMA (1932)

Background of the Case

On March 25, 1931, Ozie Powell and some friends—all African Americans—were on a freight train traveling through Alabama. Also on the train were seven white boys and two white girls. A fight took place between the African American and white boys; during the fight all the white boys but one were thrown off the train. A message was sent ahead reporting the fight and the African Americans were asked to get off the train. The two girls testified that each of them was sexually assaulted by six different African American boys in turn. They identified the seven defendants as having been among those who assaulted them.

A sheriff's posse seized the African American boys before the train reached Scottsboro, Alabama. The girls and the defendants were taken to the county seat in Scottsboro.

Prior to their arrival in Scottsboro, angry crowds had gathered after hearing about the alleged assaults. The sheriff called in the militia to protect the defendants as they were escorted to Gadsden for safekeeping and back to Scottsboro for trial a few days later. All of the defendants were described as "youthful, ignorant and illiterate." They lived in other states and had no relatives or friends to help them in their situation.

Powell and the six other African American youths were indicted on March 31 and convicted in the rapes of two white women. All were given the death penalty. The trials began six days later. There were three trials, each lasting one day. Between the times of arrest and trial, no attorney was named to represent any of the defendants. Until the very morning of the trial, no lawyer had been named to represent the defendants so they had had no time to confer with counsel.

The Alabama Supreme Court upheld the convictions, but its Chief Justice wrote a dis-sent in which he maintained the defendants had not received a fair trial. The United States Supreme Court agreed to hear the case on appeal.

Constitutional Issue

Although a number of issues were brought before the United States Supreme Court, the Court limited its examination to whether the defendants had been denied due process and the equal protection of the law because they were denied the right to counsel. Does the Fourteenth Amendment incorporate the rights of the Sixth Amendment to a speedy, fair trial in a state trial?

The Court's Decision

The Court ruled 7 to 2 in favor of Powell. Justice George Sutherland wrote the Court's decision that "in a capital case [one that is punishable by death] where the defendant is unable to employ counsel, and is incapable adequately of making his own defense . . . it is the duty of the court, whether requested or not, to assign counsel for him as a necessary requisite of due process of law." This ruling covered not only the trial itself but provided for "effective counsel" for the defendant in preparation for the trial.

In making his decision, Sutherland continued a process begun in previous cases of finding that certain rights mentioned in the Bill of Rights must also be included in the concept of due process of law. The hurdle over which all such reasoning by the Supreme Court had to pass was that the Fourteenth Amendment does not specifically mention any of these Bill of Rights protections. Quoting an earlier case, Sutherland found that the right to counsel "is of such character that it cannot be denied without violating those 'fundamental principles of liberty and justice which lie at the base of all our civil and political institutions'. . . ."

Sutherland acknowledged that the legal system too often delayed the enforcement of criminal law and that people suffered as a result. The opposite occurred in this case, however. He spoke for the defendants in this case as he wrote ". . . a defendant, charged with a serious crime, must not be stripped of his right to have sufficient time to advise with counsel and prepare his defense. To do that is not to proceed in the calm spirit of regulated justice but to go forward with the haste of the mob." He added that these defendants were tried before juries that did not include qualified members of their own race.

Therefore, Sutherland spelled out the necessity for counsel at every stage of the trial process, not just in the trial itself. Anything less, he held, constitutes a denial of due process of law.

Analyzing the Case

1. What is a capital case?

_____

_____

_____

2. What precedent had been set in earlier cases and was applied by Sutherland in his majority opinion?

_____

_____

_____

3. How does the constitutional right to a "speedy trial" apply to this case?

_____

_____

_____

Critical Thinking

4. **Making Inferences** Given the historical time in which this case took place, what factors other than legal principles might have influenced the treatment of Powell and those arrested with him?

_____

_____

_____

_____

_____

_____

_____

_____

_____

SUPREME COURT CASE 13

DE JONGE V. OREGON (1937)

Background of the Case

In July 1934, Dirk De Jonge spoke at a meeting in Portland, Oregon, organized by the local Communist party to protest police raids on workers' halls and police shootings of striking longshoremen. The meeting had been clearly represented as organized by the Communist party, and its speakers, De Jonge included, were party members. About 10 to 15 percent of the 150 to 300 people present were also party members.

In his speech, De Jonge protested conditions in the county jail, police tactics relating to the longshoremen's strike, and other matters pertaining to the strike. He also asked those present to help support the party and to purchase communist literature. The meeting went on in an orderly fashion until police raided the hall, arrested De Jonge and others, and seized a large quantity of communist literature.

De Jonge was charged and convicted under Oregon's criminal syndicalism law. This law made it a crime to publish, print, distribute, or teach criminal syndicalism, or to organize or participate in any group or assemblage advocating criminal syndicalism. Criminal syndicalism was defined as "the doctrine which advocates crime, physical violence, sabotage, or any unlawful acts or methods as a means of accomplishing or effecting industrial or political change or revolution." All these acts were felonies, punishable by up to 10 years in jail and/or a fine of up to $1,000.

Under the criminal syndicalism law, De Jonge was charged with taking part in a meeting of the Communist party, an organization that advocated criminal syndicalism and sabotage. He was convicted and sentenced to seven years' imprisonment. The judgment was upheld by the Oregon Supreme Court. De Jonge then appealed to the United States Supreme Court.

Constitutional Issue

De Jonge's defense claimed that Oregon's criminal syndicalism law violated the Fourteenth Amendment's due process clause. The Court examined that claim with a view to whether the First Amendment's guarantee of the right to assemble peaceably was to be understood as included under the Fourteenth Amendment.

The Court's Decision

The court held unanimously for De Jonge. Chief Justice Charles Evans Hughes wrote for the Court.

Hughes summarized the charge against De Jonge as follows: "His sole offense as charged . . . was that he had assisted in the conduct of a public meeting, albeit otherwise lawful, which was held under the auspices of the Communist party." As the Chief Justice pointed out, this meant that any meeting called by the Communist party to discuss any subject should result in every speaker at that meeting being convicted and jailed like De Jonge. So, while the Court agreed that states may defend themselves against attempts to replace orderly political action by revolutionary force and violence, "none of our decisions go to the length of sustaining such a curtailment of the right of free speech and assembly as the Oregon statute demands. . . ."

Since the Court held that First Amendment rights of speech and press were binding upon the states by the Fourteenth Amendment, now it found that "the right of peaceable assembly is a right cognate to those of free speech and free press and is equally fundamental. . . . For the right is one that cannot be denied without violating those fundamental principles of liberty and justice which lie at the base of all civil and political institutions, principles which the Fourteenth Amendment embodies in its due process clause."

Based on these considerations the Court concluded that it cannot be a crime to assemble peaceably for lawful discussion, to hold meetings for peaceable political action, or to assist at such meetings, no matter who sponsors them. Prosecutions are justified only for crimes committed elsewhere or for conspiracies against public peace and order. Hughes stated, however, "It is a different matter when the State, instead of prosecuting individuals for such offenses, seizes upon mere participation in a peaceable assembly and a lawful public discussion as the basis for a criminal charge."

This marked the Court's acceptance of the right to assemble as a fundamental right protected by the Fourteenth Amendment.

Analyzing the Case

1. What is criminal syndicalism?

_____

_____

_____

2. Why was the right to peaceful assembly called fundamental?

_____

_____

_____

3. What made this decision particularly significant?

_____

_____

_____

Critical Thinking

4. **Demonstrating Reasoned Judgment** Do you think that any limits should be set on the right to peaceful assembly? If so, explain what circumstances might call for such limits.

_____

_____

_____

_____

_____

_____

_____

_____

_____

_____

SUPREME COURT CASE   14

MINERSVILLE SCHOOL DISTRICT V. GOBITIS (1940)

Background of the Case

Beginning in 1898 with New York, some states began to require a flag salute ceremony as part of the opening exercises of the school day. These early state flag salute laws did not make the flag salute ceremony compulsory, but in later years many local school boards insisted that all students participate. Many patriotic organizations backed the flag salute. Opposition came from civil libertarians and some small religious groups, including the Jehovah's Witnesses.

The Jehovah's Witnesses is an evangelistic Christian sect which believes, among other things, that the biblical prohibition against worship of images forbids them to salute the flag. This religious group became the major opponent of the compulsory school flag salute.

Lillian and William Gobitis, aged 12 and 10 respectively, followed the Witnesses' teaching and refused to salute the flag in their Minersville, Pennsylvania, public schools. The Board of Education, which required a daily flag salute, expelled the children.

Since Pennsylvania made school attendance compulsory, they were placed in private schools. Their father, Walter Gobitis, then sued the Minersville Board of Education for relief from this new financial burden. He sought an injunction that would prevent the Board of Education from requiring the flag salute as a condition of free public education.

Two lower courts held in favor of Gobitis, whereupon the Minersville School District filed an appeal with the United States Supreme Court. The Minersville case became the first flag salute case to reach the Supreme Court.

Constitutional Issue

As the Court said, the issue to be decided was "whether the requirement of participation in such a ceremony, exacted from a child who refuses upon sincere religious grounds, infringes without due process of law the liberty guaranteed by the Fourteenth Amendment."

The Court's Decision

By an 8 to 1 majority, the Court decided against Gobitis. Justice Felix Frankfurter wrote for the Court.

Although individuals are protected by the Constitution in their religious beliefs or disbeliefs, Frankfurter explained that sometimes the "manifold character of man's relations may bring his conception of religious duty into conflict with the secular interests of his fellow men." As viewed by the Court, its task was "to reconcile two rights in order to prevent either from destroying the other."

Historically, Frankfurter wrote, "the religious liberty which the Constitution protects has never excluded legislation of a general scope not directed against doctrinal loyalties of particular sects." Like freedom of speech, religious freedom may sometimes necessarily be limited in order to "maintain that orderly, tranquil and free society without which religious toleration itself is unattainable."

The Court realized that this case did not deal with specific societal needs or interests such as defense, taxation, health, or family protection. However, stated Frankfurter, "all these specific activities of government presuppose the existence of an organized political society. The ultimate foundation of a free society is the binding tie of cohesive sentiment." He explained, "The precise issue, then, for us to decide is whether the legislatures of then various states . . . are barred from determining the appropriateness of various means to evoke that unifying sentiment. . . ." On that consideration, the Court declared its lack of competence to overrule the wisdom of the legislatures. "Even were we convinced of the folly of such a measure (i.e., a required flag salute), such belief would be no proof of its constitutionality." Furthermore, "the court room is not the arena for debating issues of educational policy. . . . So to hold would in effect make us the school board for the country." The Court also declined to rule that the law was unconstitutional for not making any exception to its requirements. Frankfurter concluded, "But for us to insist that, though the ceremony may be required, exceptional immunity must be given to dissidents, is to maintain that there is no basis for a legislative judgment that such an exemption might introduce elements of difficulty into the school discipline. . . ."

Analyzing the Case

1. Why did Walter Gobitis claim he needed financial relief?

_____

_____

_____

2. What, according to the Court, was the value of the flag salute?

_____

_____

_____

3. Why did the Court, in effect, refuse to overrule the lower courts?

_____

_____

_____

Critical Thinking

4. **Recognizing Ideologies** Can you think of other practices or customs, like the flag salute in schools, that Gobitis would see as possibly conflicting with constitutional principles?

_____

_____

_____

_____

_____

_____

_____

_____

SUPREME COURT CASE 15

BETTS V. BRADY (1942)

Background of the Case

Betts had been charged with robbery in Carroll County, Maryland. At his trial, Betts requested that the judge appoint counsel to represent him because he could not afford an attorney. Since local practice only required that free counsel be appointed in murder and rape cases, Betts' request was denied.

Without withdrawing his claim to court-appointed counsel, Betts conducted his own defense. He pleaded not guilty and chose to be tried without a jury. Betts was found guilty and sentenced to eight years in prison.

Constitutional Issue

In his appeal to the U.S. Supreme Court, Betts claimed that he had been denied the "due process of law" guaranteed by the Fourteenth Amendment. Specifically, Betts argued that the Sixth Amendment's guarantee of the "assistance of counsel" in all criminal prosecutions should be applicable to state trials through the matching due process clause in the Fifth and Fourteenth Amendments.

Betts' claim was based, in part, on an earlier ruling in the case of *Powell* v. *Alabama* (1932). Because the defendants had been denied the right of counsel, the Court used apparently similar reasoning to overturn a death-penalty conviction.

The Court's Decision

The Court denied Betts' claim in a 6 to 3 decision. Justice Owen Roberts wrote for the Court.

Justice Roberts carefully avoided making a "rule" that "in every case, whatever the circumstances, one charged with a crime, who is unable to obtain counsel, must be furnished counsel by the state." Each case, he stated, must be examined separately and the "totality of the facts" considered. To deny counsel might be "shocking to the universal sense of justice" in one case but not in another, the Justice wrote.

Justice Roberts reaffirmed the *Powell* decision. He noted that the trial in that case had violated "every principle of fairness," and a capital crime had been involved. Now the Court had to consider whether to enlarge that decision to include all state criminal cases.

Roberts reviewed common, colonial, and early state laws. He found that these laws could be reasonably interpreted to allow or permit a defendant to obtain counsel. However, he concluded they could not serve as a precedent "to compel the state to provide counsel for a defendant."

States had dealt previously with this matter "by statute rather than by constitutional provision," Roberts observed. The Court, then, declined to interfere with the "considered" judgment of the people, their representatives, and their courts, that appointment of counsel is not a fundamental right, essential to a fair trial." Nonetheless, "Every court has power . . . to appoint counsel where that course seems to be required in the interest of fairness," Roberts emphasized.

The Court concluded that "the Fourteenth Amendment prohibits the conviction and incarceration of one whose trial is offensive to the common and fundamental ideas of fairness and right." Roberts noted, however, that this interpretation does not include the notion that the amendment requires a defendant always to be represented by counsel.

A Dissenting Opinion

Justice Black wrote the dissenting opinion. Justice Douglas and Justice Murphy concurred.

Black felt strongly that the petitioner was denied his constitutional rights. He made the point that "the right to counsel in a criminal proceeding is fundamental." He based this on the Court's ruling in *Powell*. Further, he wrote, "It [the right to counsel] is guarded from invasion by the Sixth Amendment, adopted to raise an effective barrier against arbitrary or unjust deprivation of liberty by the federal government." He conceded that the Sixth Amendment "lays down no rule for the conduct of the states," but wrote that he felt this protection to be so fundamental to a fair trial . . . that it is made obligatory upon the states by the Fourteenth Amendment."

Referring to the fact that the petitioner was a poor, unemployed farm hand, he continued, "Denial to the poor of the request for counsel in proceedings based on charges of serious crime has long been regarded as shocking to the 'universal sense of justice' throughout this country."

Analyzing the Case

1. What did Justice Roberts find in his examination of earlier American law?

_____

_____

_____

2. Why is the Sixth Amendment not applicable directly to the states?

_____

_____

_____

3. What was the dissenting opinion as written by Justice Black?

_____

_____

_____

Critical Thinking

4. **Demonstrating Reasoned Judgment** In Justice Roberts' opinion, what serves as the ultimate guarantee of a fair trial? Do you agree or disagree? Give reasons for your answer.

_____

_____

_____

_____

_____

_____

_____

_____

_____

_____

SUPREME COURT CASE 16

WEST VIRGINIA STATE BOARD OF EDUCATION V. BARNETTE (1943)

Background of the Case

The Jehovah's Witnesses is an evangelistic Christian sect. Each of its members is considered to be a minister. Members of the Jehovah's Witnesses refuse to participate in government, bear arms or serve in the military, or salute the flag. The flag salute is forbidden on grounds that it constitutes idol worship and is forbidden by the Bible.

In 1940 the Court had decided in *Minersville School District* v. *Gobitis* that a requirement for a flag salute in public schools was not an unconstitutional infringement on religious freedom. Following that decision, West Virginia had instituted a compulsory flag salute in its public schools. Disobedience was punishable by the child's expulsion from the school and made parents liable to a 30-day jail term and a $50 fine.

For refusing to give the salute, Barnette's children and the children of other parents who were Witnesses had been expelled from their schools. State officials had threatened also to have the children sent to reformatories for criminally inclined juveniles.

Barnette sued in federal district court for an injunction against the enforcement of the flag salute law. The district court held in Barnette's favor, after which the State Board of Education appealed directly to the United States Supreme Court.

Constitutional Issue

Did West Virginia's law violate the Fourteenth Amendment's due process clause, insofar as that clause is held to include the First Amendment's protections of free exercise of religion and free speech?

The Court's Decision

The Court voted 6 to 3 that West Virginia's statute was in violation of the First and Fourteenth Amendments. Justice Robert H. Jackson delivered the Court's opinion.

Before reconsidering the *Gobitis* decision directly, Jackson pointed out that in that case the Witnesses' refusal "does not interfere with or deny rights of others. . . . The sole conflict is between authority and rights of the individual."

The Court also had "no doubt that, in connection with the pledges, the flag salute is a form of utterance. . . . It requires the individual to communicate by word and sign his acceptance of the political ideas it thus bespeaks. Objection to this form of communication when coerced is an old one, well known to the Framers of the Bill of Rights. . . . To sustain the compulsory flag salute we are required to say that a Bill of Rights, which guards the individual's right to speak his own mind, left it open to public authorities to compel him to utter what is not in his mind." Against this stood the *Gobitis* decision, which had "assumed" the state's power to impose the flag salute requirement on school children in general. The Court in the *West Virginia* case undertook to reexamine the existence of that power. In each instance it favored the individual citizen, stressing the limited nature of government under the Constitution.

Regarding citizen versus state, the Court wrote that "the Fourteenth Amendment, as now applied to the States, protects the citizen against the State itself and all of its creatures—Boards of Education not excepted." In fact, Jackson explained, the "very purpose of a Bill of Rights was to withdraw certain subjects from the vicissitudes of political controversy, to place them beyond the reach of majorities and officials and to establish them as legal principles to be applied by the courts."

The state's power to regulate is properly applied to public utilities, where the legislature can impose any rational restrictions without fear of violating the due process clause. However, wrote Jackson, "Freedoms of speech and of press, of assembly, and of worship may not be infringed on such slender grounds. They are susceptible of restriction only to prevent grave and immediate danger. It is important to note that while it is the Fourteenth Amendment which bears directly upon the State, it is the more specific limiting principles of the First Amendment that finally govern this case."

In conclusion, the Court dealt with what is called "the very heart of the *Gobitis* opinion—that the authorities had the right to select what they thought were appropriate means of fostering national unity as the basis of national security." The Court now held instead that "to believe that patriotism will not flourish if patriotic ceremonies are voluntary and spontaneous instead of a compulsory routine is to make an unflattering estimate of the appeal of our institutions to free minds. . . . We think the action of the local authorities in compelling the flag salute and pledge transcends constitutional limitations on their power and invades the sphere of intellect and spirit which it is the purpose of the First Amendment to our Constitution to reserve from all official control."

Analyzing the Case

1. How does the principle of free speech, as opposed to freedom of religion, apply to this case?

_____

_____

_____

2. What does the Court say is the basic purpose of the Bill of Rights?

_____

_____

_____

Critical Thinking

3. **Determining Relevance** Under what circumstances might the state regulate First Amendment rights? Can you cite an example of such a situation?

_____

_____

_____

_____

_____

_____

_____

_____

_____

_____

SUPREME COURT CASE 17

KOREMATSU V. UNITED STATES (1945)

Background of the Case

Following the Japanese attack on Pearl Harbor in December 1941, some authorities feared a Japanese invasion of the Pacific Coast. On the advice of the War Department, President Franklin D. Roosevelt issued Executive Order 9066. This order authorized the secretary of war to evacuate and relocate "all or any persons" in order to provide "protection against espionage and against sabotage to national defense. . . ." The order affected approximately 112,000 Japanese, about two-thirds of whom were United States citizens. An act of Congress subsequently reinforced the President's order by providing penalties for violations.

Korematsu, a Japanese American citizen, refused to leave his home in California for a relocation camp. He was convicted in federal court. An appeal to the circuit court failed. Then the case came before the United States Supreme Court.

Constitutional Issue

Since the President is the commander-in-chief of the armed forces and Congress is given the power to declare war, was the executive order and its Congressional counterpart a constitutional exercise of the war power?

The Court's Decision

By a 6 to 3 vote the Court decided against Korematsu's claim. Justice Hugo Black wrote for the Court.

The Court recently had upheld the government's position in a similar case. That case, *Hirabayashi* v. *United States* (1943) concerned the legality of a curfew order directed at persons of Japanese ancestry living in designated areas on the West Coast. In that case as well as in *Korematsu*, the Court's language pointed toward the necessity of giving the benefit of the doubt to judgments of military necessity.

In the earlier case the Court held that "we cannot reject as unfounded the judgment of the military authorities and of Congress. . . ." Likewise, in the *Korematsu* case the Court declared, "We are unable to conclude that it was beyond the war power of Congress and the Executive to exclude those of Japanese ancestry from the West Coast area at the time they did."

Justice Black cited evidence that, following internment, "approximately five thousand American citizens of Japanese ancestry refused to swear unqualified allegiance to the United States and to renounce allegiance to the Japanese Emperor, and several thousand evacuees requested repatriation to Japan." Although the Court professed itself as well aware of the hardships this program of internment imposed on American citizens, it stated that "hardships are part of war. . . . Citizenship has its responsibilities as well as its privileges, and in time of war the burden is always heavier."

The question of racial prejudice "merely confuses the issue" said the Court. The true issues are related to determining "military dangers" and "military urgency." These issues demanded that citizens of Japanese ancestry be relocated by the military authorities. Black observed, "Congress, reposing its confidence in this time of war in our military leaders. . . , determined that they should have the power to do just this. . . . The need for action was great, and the time was short. We cannot—by availing ourselves of the calm perspective of hindsight—now say that at that time these actions were unjustified."

Dissenting Opinions

Justices Frank Murphy and Robert Jackson wrote dissenting opinions. Calling the matter "this legalization of racism," Murphy objected particularly on the grounds that the Japanese Americans affected had been deprived of "equal protection of the law as guaranteed by the Fifth Amendment." Furthermore, Murphy wrote, as no provisions had been made for the hearings, "this order also deprives them of all their constitutional rights to procedural due process."

In footnotes to his dissenting opinion, Murphy pointed out that the British had faced a similar situation. They had set up 112 hearing boards which examined in six months some 74,000 German and Austrian aliens residing in Britain. Only 2,000 of these were interned. Murphy then saw no reason why this could not have been done for at least the 70,000 American citizens affected, especially since a large number of these were children or elderly men and women.

In his argument, Jackson conceded that there might have been reasonable military grounds for the internment orders. He said, "Even if they were permissible military procedures, I deny that it follows that they are constitutional. . . . A military commander may overstep the bounds of constitutionality, and it is an incident. But if we review and approve, that passing incident becomes the doctrine of the Constitution."

Analyzing the Case

1. On what authority were the evacuation orders for the removal of the Japanese Americans issued?

_____

_____

_____

2. What was the constitutional basis of Justice Murphy's dissent?

_____

_____

_____

Critical Thinking

3. **Demonstrating Reasoned Judgment** What was Justice Jackson's worry? Was this worry justified?

_____

_____

_____

_____

_____

_____

_____

_____

_____

_____

SUPREME COURT CASE   18

EVERSON V. BOARD OF EDUCATION (1947)

Background of the Case

A 1941 New Jersey law gave school districts the authority to make rules and contracts for transporting children to and from schools, including private and parochial schools.

The Board of Education for the Township of Ewing established a plan to reimburse parents for the cost of using public transportation to get their children to and from these schools.

A local taxpayer, Everson, objected to having his tax money used to pay for transporting children to religious schools. A New Jersey district court ruled in Everson's favor, noting that the 1941 law was unconstitutional under the state constitution. However, the New Jersey Court of Errors and Appeals, the state's highest court, reversed the lower court's decision.

Everson then appealed to the United States Supreme Court. Although the United States Supreme Court does not hear taxpayer cases, it agreed to rule on the First Amendment issues involved in the *Everson* case.

Constitutional Issue

The First Amendment states that "Congress shall make no law respecting establishment of religion, or prohibiting the free exercise thereof." The Court had previously ruled that this Amendment also applies to the states through the due process clause of the Fourteenth Amendment. Everson claimed that the New Jersey statute amounted to unlawful taxation in support of religion. Such action violated the First Amendment, he stressed.

The Court's Decision

In writing for a 5 to 4 majority, Justice Hugo Black reviewed the historical background of the First Amendment. He found the Amendment to be an expression of early American resentment at being taxed to support state-established churches. Accordingly, he concluded that the establishment clause of the Constitution means at least this: "Neither a state nor the federal government can set up a church. Neither can pass laws which aid one religion over another. . . . No tax in any amount, large or small, can be levied to support any religious activities or institutions, whatever they may be called, or whatever form they may adopt to teach and practice religion. . . . In the words of Jefferson, the clause against the establishment of religion by law was intended to erect 'a wall of separation between Church and State.'"

After making this pronouncement, Justice Black examined whether the New Jersey statute constituted unlawful taxation in support of religion, observing that the First Amendment also prevents a state from hampering the free exercise of religion. He reasoned that if the statute only provided for "public welfare legislation" benefiting all citizens equally, then withholding those benefits would result in discrimination against religion. Tax-subsidized bus fares, he concluded, fell into the same category as police and fire protection. Such benefits are available to the public as a whole. Black explained, "The state contributes no money to the schools. It does not support them. Its legislation . . . does no more than provide a general program to help parents get their children, regardless of their religion, safely and expeditiously to and from accredited schools."

Therefore, the Court held the 1941 New Jersey law valid, since the First Amendment only "requires the state to be neutral in its relations with groups of religious believers and nonbelievers; it does not require the state to be their adversary. State power is no more to be used so as to handicap religions than it is to favor them."

A Dissenting Opinion

Justice Wiley Rutledge disagreed with the Court's verdict. In his dissent, Justice Rutledge wrote that "the cost of transportation is no less a part of the cost of education or religious instruction than teachers or textbooks. He then wrote, "The very purpose of the state's contribution is to defray the cost of conveying the pupil to the place where he will receive not simply secular, but also and primarily religious teaching. . . ." On this ground, the reimbursement for transportation costs is not allowable.

Justice Rutledge continued to quote the writings of Presidents Madison and Jefferson often to back up his argument that the New Jersey program could not be justified as a public safety expenditure. He felt that the transportation program was, in fact, aid to church-related schools.

In the view of Justice Rutledge, "It does not make the state unneutral to withhold what the Constitution forbids it to give. On the contrary, it is only by observing the prohibition rigidly that the state can maintain its neutrality and avoid partisanship. . . ."

Analyzing the Case

1. Why did Everson claim he was being unlawfully taxed?

_____

_____

_____

2. On what principle did Justice Rutledge base his dissent?

_____

_____

_____

Critical Thinking

3. **Identifying Central Issues** How did Justice Black justify the Court's ruling to uphold the use of tax money to transport children to parochial and private schools?

_____

_____

_____

_____

_____

_____

_____

_____

_____

_____

_____

SUPREME COURT CASE 19

MCCOLLUM V. BOARD OF EDUCATION (1948)

Background of the Case

In Champaign County, Illinois, the Board of Education permitted religious teachers into school buildings to conduct classes offering 30 to 45 minutes of weekly instruction for grades four through nine. Parents signed printed cards authorizing their children to attend, and absences were reported to the school authorities. If children did not attend the religious instruction, they were given an assignment to do during this time. The religion teachers were employed by the Champaign Council on Religious Education at no cost to the schools. Classes had originally been offered for Protestant, Catholic, and Jewish students.

Mrs. Vashti McCollum, parent of a child in the Champaign school system, objected to the use of tax-supported school time and buildings for this purpose. A county court refused her petition to have these classes halted, and that decision was upheld by the Illinois Supreme Court. McCollum then appealed to the United States Supreme Court.

Constitutional Issue

Since the First Amendment prohibits any law respecting an establishment of religion or prohibiting its free exercise, did Champaign's program violate the First Amendment, as applied to the states through the due process clause of the Fourteenth Amendment?

The Court's Decision

The Court voted 8 to 1 in McCollum's favor. Justice Hugo L. Black wrote for the Court.

Black went directly to the heart of the issue. He stated that the facts of the case "show the use of the tax-supported property for religious instruction and the close cooperation between the school authorities and the religious council in promoting religious education. . . . This is beyond all question a utilization of the tax-established and tax-supported public school system to aid religious groups to spread their faith. And it falls squarely under the ban of the First Amendment (made applicable to the States by the Fourteenth). . . ."

The Court denied that rejection of McCollum's claim would "manifest a governmental hostility to religion or religious teachings. . . . The First Amendment rests upon the premise that both religion and government can best work to achieve their lofty aims if each is left free from the other within its respective sphere."

In concurring, Justice F. Frankfurter wrote, "Religious education so conducted on school time and property is patently woven into the working system of the school. The Champaign arrangement thus presents powerful elements of inherent pressure by the school system in the interest of religious sects. The fact that this power has not been used to discriminate is beside the point. Separation is a requirement to abstain from fusing functions of Government and of religious sects, not merely to treat them all equally. That a child is offered an alternative may reduce the constraint. . . . [However,] the result is an obvious pressure upon children to attend."

Frankfurter continued, "Separation means separation, not something less. Jefferson's metaphor in describing the relation between Church and State speaks of a 'wall of separation,' not of a fine line easily overstepped. The public school is at once the symbol of our democracy and the most pervasive means for promoting our common destiny. In no activity of the State is it more vital to keep out divisive forces than in its schools, to avoid confusing, not to say fusing, what the Constitution sought to keep strictly apart." Quoting the decision in *Everson* v. *Board of*

Education, Justice Frankfurter stated, "We renew our conviction that 'we have staked the very existence of our country on the faith that complete separation between the state and religion is best for the state and best for religion.'"

A Dissenting Opinion

Justice Reed was the sole dissenter. His opinion was that the Court's interpretation of the First and Fourteenth Amendments was too strict. He agreed that the nation and the states were not to make law regarding establishment of religion, but he felt, "A state is entitled to have great leeway in its legislation when dealing with the important social problems of its populations. . . . Devotion to the great principle of religious liberty should not lead us into a rigid interpretation of the constitutional guarantee that conflicts with accepted habits of our people."

Analyzing the Case

1. Who employed the religious teachers in this case?

_____

_____

_____

2. In what way was the state held to be supporting religion?

_____

_____

_____

3. According to the decision, what is the best relationship between government and religion under the First Amendment?

_____

_____

_____

Critical Thinking

4. **Demonstrating Reasoned Judgment** Do you agree with the Court's decision in this case? Explain your answer.

_____

_____

_____

_____

_____

_____

_____

_____

_____

SUPREME COURT CASE 20

DENNIS V. UNITED STATES (1951)

Background of the Case

In 1948, Eugene Dennis and ten co-defendants, all leaders of the United States Communist party, were convicted for violating the Smith Act, a federal law passed in 1940. That law made it illegal to teach or advocate the violent overthrow of the United States government. It was also forbidden to publish such advocacy, to organize a group advocating such policies, to belong to such a group, or to conspire to do any such thing. Their trial in New York District Court lasted about nine months and took nearly 16,000 pages to record.

In his instructions to the jury the trial judge said that it would not be enough to convict the defendants if they had only taught or conspired to teach subversion. He stated, "You must be satisfied . . . that the defendants had an intent to cause the overthrow or destruction of the Government of the United States by force and violence" and that they had organized the Communist party for this purpose.

The defendants appealed their convictions to the United States Supreme Court, maintaining that their rights to freedom of speech had been compromised. The legal composition of the jury was also questioned. The United States Supreme Court, however, dealt only with Sections 2 and 3 of the Smith Act and their relationship to the Bill of Rights and the First and Fifth Amendments.

Constitutional Issue

The central questions in this case were: Did the Smith Act unconstitutionally limit free press and speech under the First Amendment? Did the act conflict with the Fifth Amendment's guarantee of due process of law?

The Court's Decision

The Court held 6 to 2 that the statute was constitutional. The Court limited itself to an examination of the Smith Act's constitutionality and did not reconsider the lower court's ruling that the defendants had in fact advocated or conspired to overthrow the United States government. Chief Justice Fred Vinson wrote for the majority.

The Court first supported the power of Congress to protect itself against rebellion, especially since "the existing structure of the government provides for peaceful and orderly change." The true question, however, "is not whether Congress has such <u>power</u>, but whether the <u>means</u> conflict with the First and Fifth Amendments to the Constitution."

The defendants had claimed that the Smith Act amounted to a prohibition even of academic discussion of Marxist thought. The Court rejected the contention, stating "it is directed at advocacy, not discussion."

At this point the Court's examination shifted to the circumstances under which free speech may be limited. The primary precedent case had been *Schenck* v. *United States* (1919), in which Justice Oliver Wendell Holmes had devised the "clear and present danger" test. Holmes explained, "The question in every case is whether the words used are of such a nature as to create a clear and present danger that they will bring about the substantive evils that Congress has a right to prevent."

Since *Schenck,* there had been a number of cases in which the "clear and present danger" test had been variously applied or found not applicable. The phrase "clear and present danger" had developed along rather complex lines in such a way that Vinson now felt that a more precise determination of its meaning had become necessary.

Vinson cited the opinion of the first appeals judge in the *Dennis* case, Chief Judge Learned Hand. Hand interpreted "clear and present danger" this way: "In each case [courts] must ask whether the gravity of the 'evil,' discounted by its improbability, justifies such invasion of free speech as is necessary to avoid the danger." Vinson accepted this interpretation, generally abbreviated as having changed "clear and present" to "clear and probable" danger.

On this new ground, the Court could deal easily with the issues of conspiracy and advocacy. The Communist party of the United States of America was characterized as "a highly organized conspiracy, with rigidly dis-ciplined members subject to call when the leaders . . . felt that the time had come for action." In other words, the danger or threat of rebellion already existed, although no overt action had been taken yet. Holmes concluded that "this analysis disposes of the contention that a conspiracy to advocate, as distinguished from the advocacy itself, cannot be constitutionally restrained, because it comprises only presentation. It is the existence of the conspiracy which creates the danger. . . ."

Analyzing the Case

1. What was the purpose of the Smith Act?

_____

_____

_____

2. According to the majority decision in the *Dennis* case, why was the Smith Act deemed constitutional?

_____

_____

_____

Critical Thinking

3. **Demonstrating Reasoned Judgment** Why should people who belong to a group whose objectives are clearly opposed to democratic principles be protected by the United States Constitution or other laws? Give reasons for your answer.

_____

_____

_____

_____

_____

_____

_____

_____

_____

_____

SUPREME COURT CASE   21

FEINER V. NEW YORK (1951)

Background of the Case

One evening in March of 1949, Irving Feiner was addressing an open-air meeting on a street corner in Syracuse, New York. Feiner, a student at Syracuse University, spoke to a mixed-race crowd of about 75 people. He denounced various national and local officials and reportedly sought "to arouse the Negro people against the whites, urging that they rise up in arms and fight for equal rights."

Two policemen, who had been watching from across the street, stepped in to urge people out of the path of traffic and back onto the sidewalk. After a while, the crowd grew restless and unruly, and the officers believed that a fight was imminent. Some of the crowd made comments to the officers about their inability to handle the crowd.

At least one person threatened violence if the police did not act. Several times over the next few minutes the police requested that Feiner cease speaking; Feiner ignored them. Finally, Feiner was arrested, charged with disorderly conduct, and later convicted. Three lower courts subsequently upheld that verdict, after which Feiner appealed to the United States Supreme Court.

Constitutional Issue

The First Amendment guarantees the right of free speech and is applicable to the states through the due process clause of the Fourteenth Amendment. Does this right prevent police from interfering when they believe free speech threatens to incite hearers to violate public order?

The Court's Decision

Chief Justice Fred Vinson wrote for the 6 to 3 majority. Feiner's conviction was upheld as constitutional.

The Court found the lower court records persuasive as to the threat of impending crowd disorder. The principle they applied was derived from *Cantwell* v. *Connecticut* (1940): "When clear and present danger of riot, disorder, interference with traffic upon the public streets, or other immediate threat to public safety, peace, or order appears, the power of the state to prevent or punish is obvious."

In agreeing with the lower courts' finding, Vinson wrote, "It is one thing to say that the police cannot be used as an instrument for the suppression of unpopular views, and another to say that, when as here the speaker passes the bounds of argument or persuasion and undertakes incitement to riot, they are powerless to prevent a breach of the peace. Nor in this case can we condemn the considered judgment of three New York courts approving the means which the police, faced with a crisis, used in the exercise of their power and duty to preserve peace and order. The findings of the state courts as to the existing situation and the imminence of greater disorder coupled with the petitioner's deliberate defiance of the police officers convince us that we should not reverse this conviction in the name of free speech."

The Court said it was well aware of the dangers of allowing a hostile audience to prevent someone from speaking or "the possible danger of giving overzealous police officials complete discretion to break up otherwise lawful public meetings. . . ." Nevertheless, Vinson wrote, the Court was unwilling to rule that the police had not properly used their power to preserve order in this instance.

A Dissenting Opinion

Justices Hugo Black and William O. Douglas each wrote dissents on largely identical grounds. Both thought, in Black's words, that "if, in the name of preserving order, [the police] ever can interfere with a lawful public speaker, they first must make all reasonable efforts to protect him. . . . Their duty was to protect the petitioner's right to talk. . . . Instead they suppressed that duty and acted only to suppress the right to speak." Black further argued, "A speaker may not, of course, incite a riot. . . . It is against that kind of threat that speakers need police protection (i.e., against an unsympathetic audience). If they do not receive it and instead the police throw their weight on the side of those who would break up the meetings, the police become the new censors of speech."

In a strong statement against the Court's ruling, Black wrote, "I think this conviction makes a mockery of the free speech guarantees of the First and Fourteenth Amendments. The end result . . . is to approve a simple and readily available technique by which cities and states can with impunity subject all speeches, political or otherwise, on streets or elsewhere, to the supervision and censorship of the local police. I will have no part or parcel in this holding which I view as a long step toward totalitarian authority."

Analyzing the Case

1. What was the charge against Feiner?

_____

_____

_____

2. Of what importance was the decision in the *Cantwell* case to Feiner?

_____

_____

_____

Critical Thinking

3. **Demonstrating Reasoned Judgment** Do you agree or disagree with Black's dissent? On what basis?

_____

_____

_____

_____

_____

_____

_____

_____

_____

_____

_____

SUPREME COURT CASE   22

BROWN V. BOARD OF EDUCATION OF TOPEKA, KANSAS (1954)

Background of the Case

Brown represents a collection of cases, all decided together. The cases had one common feature: African American children had been denied admission to segregated white public schools.

These cases reached the U.S. Supreme Court by way of appeals through lower courts, all of which had ruled in accordance with the decision in *Plessy* v. *Ferguson* (1896). The Plessy case determined that separate but equal facilities did not violate the Fourteenth Amendment's guarantee of "equal protection of the law."

An earlier case, *Sweatt* v. *Painter* (1950) had held that African Americans must be admitted to the previously segregated University of Texas Law School because no separate but equal facility existed in the state. In *Brown,* however, there were findings "that the Negro and white schools involved have been equalized or were being equalized. . . ."

Constitutional Issue

The *Brown* case was an explicit reappraisal of the question in *Plessy* v. *Ferguson*. Did separate but equal public facilities violate the equal protection clause of the Fourteenth Amendment?

The Court's Decision

Chief Justice Earl Warren wrote the Court's unanimous decision.

Justice Warren began by noting that attempts to determine the precise intent of the Fourteenth Amendment's original sponsors have proved inconclusive. Even more difficult was any effort to discover its relation to the issue of public schools, as so few were in existence when the Amendment took effect.

Warren explained that the Court's method of examination, then, was to "look to the effect of segregation itself on public education" in order to determine "if segregation in public schools deprives these plaintiffs of the equal protection of the law." Warren added, "In approaching this problem, we cannot turn the clock back to 1868 when the [Fourteenth] Amendment was adopted, or even to 1896 when *Plessy* v. *Ferguson* was written. We must consider public education in the light of its full development and its present place in American life throughout the Nation. . . . Only in this way can it be determined if segregation in public schools deprives these plaintiffs of the equal protection of the law."

Warren quoted a Kansas state court ruling, which held that "segregation with the sanction of law, therefore, has a tendency to retard the educational and mental development of Negro children and to deprive them of some of the benefits they would receive in a racially integrated school system." Likewise, the U. S. Supreme Court concluded that segregation of African American schoolchildren "generates a feeling of inferiority as to their status in the community that may affect their hearts and minds in a way unlikely ever to be undone."

Recognizing further the huge psychological impact of segregation, Warren quoted the finding of a lower court with which he agreed (even though that court did rule against the plaintiffs). That lower court stated the finding based on psychological authority that, "Segregation of white and colored children in public schools has a detrimental effect upon the colored children. The impact is greater when it has the sanction of the law; for the policy of separating the races is usually interpreted as denoting the inferiority of the Negro group. A sense of inferiority affects the motivation of a child to learn. Segregation with the sanction of law, therefore, has the tendency to [retard] the education and mental development of Negro children and to deprive them of some of the benefits they would receive in a racially integrated school system."

Agreeing with this statement, Warren concluded, "Whatever may have been the extent of psychological knowledge at the time of *Plessy* v. *Ferguson,* this finding is amply supported by modern authority. Any language in *Plessy* v. *Ferguson* contrary to this finding is rejected."

On this basis the Court concluded "that in the field of public education the doctrine of 'separate but equal' has no place. Separate educational facilities are inherently unequal. Therefore we hold that the plaintiffs and others similarly situated for whom the actions have been brought are, by reason of the segregation complained of, deprived of the equal protection of the law guaranteed by the Fourteenth Amendment. This disposition makes unnecessary any discussion whether such segregation also violates the due process clause of the Fourteenth Amendment."

Analyzing the Case

1. How does the *Brown* case differ from *Sweatt* v. *Painter?*

_____

_____

_____

2. What was the question raised by both *Plessy* and *Brown?*

_____

_____

_____

3. On what basis did the Court reach its decision in *Brown?*

_____

_____

_____

Critical Thinking

4. Evaluating Information How would you have interpreted the phrase "separate but equal"? Do you agree or disagree with the ruling in the *Brown* case? Explain your answer.

_____

_____

_____

_____

_____

_____

_____

SUPREME COURT CASE 23

YATES V. UNITED STATES (1957)

Background of the Case

Oleta O'Connor Yates was one of 14 leaders of the Communist party in California. All were charged under the Smith Act of 1940 with conspiracy to teach and advocate the violent overthrow of the United States government, and with organizing the Communist party for that purpose. All were found guilty, fined $10,000, and sentenced to five years in jail. They appealed their convictions to a federal court, which upheld the trial court's judgment. However, the United States Supreme Court agreed to review their appeals (grouped under Yates' name) in order to reexamine and refine its decision in *Dennis* v. *United States* (1951).

Constitutional Issue

A substantially identical question of Communist party organization in violation of the Smith Act was the focus of the *Dennis* case. The Court had held that the Smith Act did not violate First Amendment protections of speech and press. Furthermore, the Court had concluded in *Dennis* that the defendants' purpose had been the ultimate overthrow of the United States government by force; the mere fact that they had not yet put their plans into action was held to be no defense.

The *Dennis* decision had been generally understood as a modification of the decision in *Schenck* v. *United States* (1919), which had held that the protection of the First Amendment needed to be weighed against the question of whether there was some "clear and present danger" to the government. The *Dennis* case had modified this formulation to a consideration of whether some danger was not only <u>present</u> but <u>probable</u>.

The precise question at issue, then, was whether simple advocacy of violent governmental overthrow was prohibited. Did advocacy have to be accompanied by actual incitement to action in order to override the protections of the First Amendment?

The Court's Decision

On constitutional grounds, all the original convictions in the *Yates* case were reversed. However, based on the Supreme Court's review of the original trial record, five defendants were acquitted and new trials ordered for the other nine. Justice John M. Harlan wrote for the majority.

Harlan's examination centered around the trial judge's instructions to the jury. The judge had not informed the jury that it would be necessary to prove that any advocacy to overthrow the government had also intended to incite people to take such action. Both the prosecution and the defense had suggested such instructions, but the trial judge had rejected the suggestions on the grounds that the decision in *Dennis* made this unnecessary. In other words, the trial judge had interpreted *Dennis* as requiring only that intent to forcibly overthrow the government need to be shown, that it was unnecessary to prove actual incitement to action. Justice Harlan wrote that "we are thus faced with the question whether the Smith Act prohibits advocacy and teaching of forcible overthrow as an abstract principle, divorced from any effort to instigate action to that end, so long as such advocacy or teaching is engaged in with evil intent. We hold that it does not."

The Court found that "the legislative history of the Smith Act and related bills shows beyond all question that Congress was aware of the distinction between the advocacy or teaching of abstract doctrine and the advocacy or teaching of action, and that it did not intend to disregard it. The statute was aimed at the advocacy and teaching of concrete action . . . and not of principles divorced from action."

The Court defined the distinction between *Dennis* and *Yates*. In *Dennis*, "advocacy was aimed at building up a seditious group and maintaining it in readiness for action at a propitious time. . . ." The district judge in the *Yates* case had been under the impression that "mere doctrinal justification of forcible overthrow, if engaged in with the intent to accomplish overthrow, is punishable per se under the Smith Act." Harlan called the latter "too remote from concrete action" to fall under the standard announced in *Dennis*. "The essential distinction is that those to whom the advocacy is addressed must be urged to do something, now or in the future, rather than merely to <u>believe</u> in something." The Court recognized that these distinctions "are often subtle and difficult to grasp." For that very reason, the trial judge ought to have given more adequate instructions to the jury.

Finally, it should be noted that the *Yates* case, although it claims not to overturn the *Dennis* decision, was effectively understood as having signalled a return to the pre-*Dennis* standard that "clear and present danger" must always be proved before First Amendment rights can be limited.

Analyzing the Case

1. What is the difference between advocacy and incitement?

_____

_____

_____

2. On what did the trial judge in the *Dennis* case base his decision?

_____

_____

_____

Critical Thinking

3. Synthesizing Information Compare the standards in *Schenck* and *Dennis*. How did they influence the *Yates* case?

_____

_____

_____

_____

_____

_____

_____

_____

_____

_____

_____

SUPREME COURT CASE   24

MAPP V. OHIO (1961)

Background of the Case

On May 23, 1957, three Cleveland police officers arrived at Miss Mapp's home after having received a tip that a fugitive had hidden there. Mapp, who had phoned her attorney, refused to admit the police. They notified their headquarters, and the officers began surveillance.

Three hours later four more officers arrived and knocked on the door. When Mapp did not immediately answer, the police forced the door and entered. Mapp, from halfway up the stairs, demanded to see a search warrant. One of the officers held up a piece of paper, claiming it was the warrant. Mapp snatched the paper and stuffed it into her blouse. After a scuffle, the officers recovered the paper and handcuffed Mapp.

Mapp, still handcuffed, was forced upstairs, whereupon the police began to search the entire house. During this time, Mapp's attorney arrived but was refused entrance or access to his client.

No fugitive was discovered. However, in the course of their search, police turned up some material deemed obscene. Mapp was charged and eventually convicted of having had lewd and lascivious books and pictures in her possession, a violation of an Ohio statute.

At her trial, no search warrant was ever produced, nor was the failure to produce one explained or accounted for. On appeal, the Supreme Court of Ohio held that her conviction was valid even though the evidence had been illegally seized. Mapp appealed her case to the United States Supreme Court, which caused other facts to be revealed about her treatment by the police officers and her rights concerning search and seizure.

Constitutional Issue

The *Mapp* case functioned both to deepen the principle and to overturn the application of the decision in *Wolf* v. *Colorado* (1949). *Wolf* had recognized a basic right to privacy stemming from the Fourth Amendment provision against unreasonable searches and seizures. "It is therefore implicit in 'the concept of ordered liberty' and as such enforceable against the States through the due process clause."

Even so, the Court had declined to forbid illegally seized evidence from being used at trial for two reasons. First, the general tendency of common law was to admit such evidence, holding that it was not really a court's concern as to how evidence had been obtained, only that it was good evidence. Second, the Court in *Wolf* had reasoned that local authorities and local public opinion would act as effective restraints on oppressive action by the police.

The question for Mapp was whether the right to privacy implied in the Fourth Amendment, as applied to the states through the due process clause of the Fourteenth Amendment, prohibits the use of illegally seized evidence in state courts.

The Court's Decision

The Court voted 6 to 3 to reverse the Ohio Supreme Court's decision. Justice Tom C. Clark wrote for the majority.

Justice Clark viewed the new ruling as the necessary completion of the *Wolf* opinion. He stated, "In extending the substantive protections of due process to all constitutionally unreasonable searches—state or federal—it was logically and constitutionally necessary that the exclusion doctrine—an essential part of the right to privacy—be also insisted upon as an essential ingredient of the right newly recognized by the *Wolf* case." The Court held that this new right could not continue to tolerate the admission of unlawfully seized evidence. The *Mapp* decision was seen by the Court as the end to a double standard by which "a federal prosecutor may make no use of evidence illegally seized, but a State's attorney across the street may. . . ." Justice Clark wrote that this decision also ended an unfortunate situation in which "the State, by admitting evidence unlawfully seized, serves to encourage disobedience to the Federal Constitution which it is bound to uphold."

Clark was aware that the Court's ruling would sometimes result in criminals going free because of an error on the part of police. To this possibility he replied, "The criminal goes free, if he must, but it is the law that sets him free. Nothing can destroy a government more quickly than its failure to observe its own laws, or worse, its disregard of the charter of its own existence. . . . On any other course, the right to privacy would remain merely "an empty promise," Clark observed.

Analyzing the Case

1. What is the basis for the right of privacy?

_____

_____

_____

2. How can the Fourth Amendment be applied to the states?

_____

_____

_____

3. What was the "double standard" referred to in the decision?

_____

_____

_____

Critical Thinking

4. **Demonstrating Reasoned Judgment** Do you agree with the decision in this case? Explain your answer.

_____

_____

_____

_____

_____

_____

_____

_____

_____

SUPREME COURT CASE   25

BAKER V. *CARR* (1962)

Background of the Case

Tennessee's legislature consisted of a 33-member Senate and a 99-member House of Representatives. These legislators were to be apportioned among the counties according to population. The state constitution provided for reapportionment based on the United States census, taken once every 10 years.

As of 1959, when Baker brought suit on his own behalf and that of other Tennessee voters, no reapportionment had been made since 1901. Population changes since then resulted in substantial inequalities between voting districts, sometimes on the order of 4 to 1. The consequence was that less than half the voters could elect sizeable majorities in both houses.

Repeated attempts to force reapportionment had all been rejected by the legislature. Baker sued Tennessee's secretary of state, Carr, for relief from denial of equal protection of the law under the Fourteenth Amendment. A federal district court dismissed the case as presenting a political question beyond the competence of the judiciary.

Constitutional Issue

The central issue in the *Baker* case concerned the Fourteenth Amendment rights. Yet the district court was of the opinion that it lacked jurisdiction in the matter. The question considered by the Supreme Court, then, was whether, under Article III, Section 2, of the Constitution, federal courts had jurisdiction to consider cases of state reapportionment. If so, could the case be decided by a court—was it "justiciable"?

The Court's Decision

The Court voted 6 to 2 in favor of the federal district court's jurisdiction and, decided that the case was justiciable.

Justice William Brennan, who wrote the decision for the Court, dealt simply with the question of jurisdiction and whether the case was justiciable. Jurisdiction had been declined because the district court thought the case would involve impermissible political questions. Since no such political questions were present, the matter therefore had to be subject to judicial inquiry—it qualified as a case or controversy arising under the Constitution in accord with Article III, Section 2.

Brennan explained why the matter was considered justiciable. He noted, "The mere fact that the suit seeks protection of a political right does not mean it presents a political question."

A prime example of a political question would be one arising from the guaranty clause of Article IV, Section 4, which guarantees each state a republican form of government. The Court, however, has always held that "the guarantee clause is not a repository of judicially manageable standards which a court could utilize independently in order to identify a State's lawful government." Other examples of nonjusticiable political questions are matters concerning Native American nations, foreign relations, and, in general, matters that are properly the concern of the executive or legislative branches under the separation of powers.

After lengthy consideration, Brennan concluded that no political question was involved. He stated, "The question here is the consistency of state action with the Federal Constitution. We have no question decided, or to be decided, by a political branch of government co-equal with this Court. . . . Nor need the appellants, in order to succeed in this action, ask the Court to enter upon policy determinations for which judicially manageable standards are lacking. Judicial standards under the equal protection clause are well-developed and familiar. . . ." The decision in *Baker* v. *Carr* was the first to hold that federal courts could hear suits challenging voting district apportionment.

A Dissenting Opinion

Justice Frankfurter wrote a dissenting opinion which reads, "In effect, today's decision empowers the courts of the country to devise what should constitute the proper composition of the legislatures of the fifty states." He said that if the state courts could not solve this question, the ruling in this case now made the Supreme Court ultimately the decision-maker in such cases.

Disagreeing, he wrote, "The Framers carefully and with deliberate forethought refused to so enthrone the judiciary. In this situation . . . appeal for relief does not belong here. Appeal must be to an informed, civically militant electorate." In summary, Frankfurter felt that the Supreme Court should not be the source of decisions about state legislative reapportionment. He felt that there was no constitutional justification for the Court's decision in this case and that the ruling would send the lower courts into a "mathematical quagmire."

Analyzing the Case

1. What are some examples of nonjusticiable political questions?

_____

_____

_____

2. What is the purpose of the guaranty clause?

_____

_____

Critical Thinking

3. **Identifying Central Issues** On what grounds did the Court hold that Baker's claim could be decided by a federal court?

_____

_____

_____

_____

_____

_____

_____

_____

_____

_____

_____

SUPREME COURT CASE 26

ENGEL V. VITALE (1962)

Background of the Case

In 1951 the New York State Board of Regents, which supervises the state's public school system, approved a brief prayer for recital in the schools at the start of each day. It read: "Almighty God, we acknowledge our dependence upon Thee, and we beg Thy blessings upon us, our parents, our teachers, and our Country." In 1958 the New Hyde Park school board adopted the prayer and directed that it be said aloud each day in every class.

Steven Engel, the father of two children in New Hyde Park schools, objected. He asked a state court to order that the prayer be dropped. Engel directed his suit against William J. Vitale, Jr., head of the school board. That court and the New York Court of Appeals denied his request. He then appealed to the United States Supreme Court, which agreed to hear the case.

Constitutional Issue

The First Amendment, applied to the states through the due process clause of the Fourteenth Amendment, prohibits laws respecting an establishment of religion or its free exercise. Did the daily prayer, although noncompulsory, violate the First Amendment?

The Court's Decision

The Court ruled 6 to 1 in Engel's favor. Justice Hugo Black wrote the majority opinion.

No one had contested that the prayer was essentially religious. Vitale had argued, however, that it was permissible because it was "nondenominational." Furthermore, Vitale noted that no student was compelled either to say the prayer or to remain in the classroom while it was being said.

The Supreme Court disagreed, calling the practice "wholly inconsistent with the estab-lishment clause." It agreed that a prayer "composed by government officials as part of a government program to further religious beliefs . . . breaches the constitutional wall of separation between Church and State." Black pointed out, "It is a matter of history that this very practice of establishing governmen-tally composed prayers for religious services was one of the reasons which caused many of our early colonists to leave England and seek religious freedom in America."

In the Court's view, "the First Amendment was added to the Constitution to stand as a guarantee that neither the power nor the prestige of the Federal Government would be used to control, sup-port, or influence the kinds of prayers the American people can say. . . . Under that Amendment's prohibition . . . government in this country . . . is without power to pre-scribe any particular form of prayer which is to be used as an official prayer in carrying on any program of governmentally sponsored religious activity."

Black specified several purposes of the establishment clause. Among them, the clause sought (a) to prevent the "union of government and religion (which) tends to destroy government and to degrade reli-gion"; (b) to express the principle "that reli-gion is too personal, too sacred, too holy, to permit its 'unhallowed perversion' by a civil magistrate"; and (c) to prevent religious per-secutions which have historically arisen from governmentally established religions.

The nation, the Constitution, and the Bill of Rights were all established in order to avoid these sorts of problems, Black conclud-ed. Therefore, "the New York laws officially prescribing the Regents' prayer are inconsis-tent both with the purposes of the establish-ment clause and with the establishment clause itself."

A Dissenting Opinion

Justice P. Stewart dissented as he wrote, in part, "The Court does not hold, nor could it, that New York has interfered with the free exercise of anybody's religion. For the state courts have made it clear that those who object to reciting the prayer may be entirely free of any compulsion to do so, including any 'embarrassments and pressures.' . . . But the Court says that in permitting schoolchildren to say this simple prayer, the New York authorities have established 'an official religion.' With all respect, I think the Court has misapplied a great constitutional principle. I cannot see how an official religion is established by letting those who want to say a prayer say it." He continued, "On the contrary, I think that to deny the wish of these schoolchildren to join in reciting this prayer is to deny them the opportunity of sharing in the spiritual heritage of our Nation."

Analyzing the Case

1. What two things does the First Amendment prohibit?

_____

_____

_____

2. Why did Vitale maintain that the school prayer was constitutional?

_____

_____

_____

3. What historical argument against this prayer did Black cite?

_____

_____

_____

Critical Thinking

4. **Demonstrating Reasoned Judgment** The Constitution lays down the principle of church-state separation. However, United States coins and paper money carry the phrase "In God We Trust." Does a constitutional conflict exist in this instance? Explain your answer.

_____

_____

_____

_____

_____

_____

_____

_____

_____

SUPREME COURT CASE 27

ABINGTON SCHOOL DISTRICT V. SCHEMPP (1963)

Background of the Case

Two cases were decided in one opinion: *Abington School District* v. *Schempp* and *Murray* v. *Curlett*. In the *Abington* case, Pennsylvania law required that "at least ten verses from the Holy Bible shall be read, without comment, at the opening of each public school on each school day. Any child shall be excused from such Bible reading . . . upon the written request of his parent or guardian."

Two children of the Schempp family were enrolled in Abington public schools. The Schempps objected to the readings because Unitarians do not hold that the Bible is always intelligible when read literally. Further, they objected to having their children sent out into the hallway during readings. They claimed that the practice violated their rights under the First Amendment and brought suit to have the practice abandoned. A federal district court sided with the Schempps and found Pennsylvania's law unconstitutional.

In the *Murray* case, William Murray objected to a Baltimore, Maryland, school board rule that allowed for daily readings in the classroom of a Bible chapter or the Lord's prayer. The local statute was in accordance with state law at the time. Murray and his son, a student in the Baltimore school system, objected as atheists to the doctrine of a God as the "source of all moral and spiritual values," and to the Bible itself, which they characterized as "nauseating, historically inaccurate, replete with the ravings of madmen."

Still, a Maryland appeals court supported the school board. The state's highest court agreed, whereupon the Murrays appealed to the United States Supreme Court.

Constitutional Issue

The issue in both cases was whether the First Amendment's prohibition of governmental support of the establishment of religion, made binding on the states by the due process clause of the Fourteenth Amendment, was violated by Bible recitation in public schools.

The Court's Decision

The Court ruled in an 8 to 1 decision that "the practices at issue and the laws requiring them are unconstitutional under the establishment clause." Justice Tom C. Clark wrote for the Court.

The Court pointed both to the American tradition of religious belief and to its tradition of religious freedom. It reaffirmed earlier rulings that civil authority and religious activity must remain separate, and that no support of religion could be given from public sources. In testing a law for violation of either the establishment clause or the free exercise clause, the Court's rule was that the law must neither advance nor inhibit religion.

The state in both cases insisted that its Bible readings served "secular purposes . . . the promotion of moral values, the contradiction to the materialistic trends of our times, the perpetuation of our institutions and the teachings of literature." The Supreme Court, however, found that the use of the Bible for these purposes constituted a religious ceremony. The Bible might properly be used for historical or literary studies, "but the exercises here do not fall into those categories. They are religious exercises, required by the States in violation of the command of the First Amendment that the Government maintain strict neutrality, neither aiding nor opposing religion."

In his concluding statement, Clark echoed the sentiments of the majority of the Court as he wrote, "The place of religion in our society is an exalted one, achieved through a long tradition of reliance on the home, the church, and the inviolable citadel of the heart and mind. We have come to recognize through bitter experience that it is not within the power of government to invade that citadel, whether its purpose or effect be to aid or oppose, to advance or retard. In the relationship between man and religion, the State is firmly committed to a position of neutrality. Though the application of that rule requires interpretation of a delicate sort, the rule itself is clearly and concisely stated in the words of the First Amendment."

A Dissenting Opinion

Justice P. Stewart was the only voice of dissent. His concerns were mainly that the rights of other children to take part in a religious prayer exercise were being denied. He made the point that the prayers in question were not being forced upon any children who did not wish to participate and he expressed the fear that "all school boards might find it impossible to administer a system of religious exercises during school hours in such a way to meet this constitutional standard."

Analyzing the Case

1. Was the use of the Bible entirely prohibited in public schools?

_____

_____

_____

2. What position must the government take regarding religion?

_____

_____

_____

Critical Thinking

3. **Identifying Central Issues** Why did both states consider the Bible readings constitutional?

_____

_____

_____

_____

_____

_____

_____

_____

_____

_____

_____

_____

SUPREME COURT CASE   28

GIDEON V. WAINWRIGHT (1963)

Background of the Case

Clarence Earl Gideon was arrested for breaking into a Florida pool hall with the intention to burglarize it. At trial the court refused his request for a court-appointed attorney, since Florida provided free counsel only in capital cases.

Gideon pleaded not guilty and conducted his own defense. He was found guilty and sentenced to five years' imprisonment. From prison Gideon submitted a handwritten petition requesting the United States Supreme Court to accept his case on appeal. Such a petition is called *in forma pauperis*, or "as a pauper." In such cases the Court may accept petitions from indigent individuals and then appoint counsel to represent them before the Court. In the *Gideon* case, the Court appointed Abe Fortas as his attorney.

Constitutional Issue

Gideon's case was taken by the Court in order to reconsider the decision in *Betts* v. *Brady* (1942). In *Betts*, the Court had held that, outside of special circumstances, the due process clause of the Fourteenth Amendment did not require the application of the Sixth Amendment's guarantee of counsel in criminal cases to state trials. An earlier decision, *Powell* v. *Alabama* (1932), had ensured that state courts would provide counsel in capital cases.

The Court's Decision

The Court found in Gideon's favor, overturning *Betts* v. *Brady*. Justice Hugo Black wrote for the unanimous Court.

Basically, Justice Black observed, the Court accepted the theoretical standard of the *Betts* decision. "A provision of the Bill of Rights which is 'fundamental and essential to a fair trial' is made obligatory on the States by the Fourteenth Amendment," he wrote. The *Gideon* ruling simply placed the right to

counsel in all criminal cases among these essential provisions.

Black's opinion was that the decision in *Betts* represented an abrupt break from precedents such as those found in *Powell*. These precedents, he stressed, as well as "reason and reflection," convinced the Court that "in our adversary system of criminal justice, any person haled [brought] into court, who is too poor to hire a lawyer, cannot be assured a fair trial unless counsel is provided for him."

Black went on to stress that poor and rich alike are entitled to counsel. He wrote, "Governments . . . spend vast sums of money . . . to try defendants. Lawyers to prosecute are everywhere deemed essential to protect the public's interest in an orderly society. Similarly, there are few defendants charged with crime, few indeed, who fail to hire the best lawyers they can get to prepare and present their defenses. That government hires lawyers to prosecute and defendants who have money hire lawyers to defend are the strongest indications of the widespread belief that lawyers in criminal courts are necessities, not luxuries. The right of one charged with a crime to counsel may not be deemed fundamental and essential for fair trials in some countries, but it is in ours."

He continued, "From the very beginning, our state and national constitutions and laws have laid great emphasis on procedural and substantive safeguards designed to assure fair trials before impartial tribunals in which every defendant stands equal before the law. This noble ideal cannot be realized if the poor man charged with crime has to face his accusers without a lawyer to assist him."

In making the point that Gideon, like most people, did not have the expertise to defend himself, Black quoted the words of Justice Sutherland in *Powell* v. *Alabama:* "The right to be heard would be, in many cases, of little avail if it did not comprehend the right to be heard by counsel. Even the intelligent and educated layman has small and sometimes no skill in the science of law. If charged with crime, he is incapable, generally, of determining for himself whether the indictment is good or bad. Left without the aid of counsel he may be put on trial without a proper charge, and convicted upon incompetent evidence, or evidence irrelevant to the issue or otherwise inadmissible. He lacks both the skill and knowledge adequately to prepare his defense, even though he may have a perfect one. He requires the guiding hand of counsel at every step of the proceedings against him. Without it, though he be not guilty, he faces the danger of conviction because he does not know how to establish his innocence."

Gideon won a retrial, this time with the assistance of a court-appointed attorney. Before the same judge and in the same courtroom, Gideon was acquitted.

Analyzing the Case

1. What action did Gideon take while in prison?

_____

_____

_____

2. In the *Gideon* case, did the Court uphold the decision found previously in *Betts* v. *Brady*?

_____

_____

_____

3. Why did Black feel Gideon could not represent himself?

_____

_____

_____

Critical Thinking

4. **Identifying Central Issues** Why did Black feel so strongly that ability to pay for a lawyer should not be the deciding factor in a trial?

_____

_____

_____

_____

_____

_____

_____

_____

SUPREME COURT CASE 29

ESCOBEDO V. ILLINOIS (1964)

Background of the Case

Danny Escobedo was arrested for the murder of his brother-in-law in Chicago. The arrest took place at 2:30 A.M. the morning after the fatal shooting. Escobedo was arrested without a warrant and interrogated. The police never informed Escobedo of his constitutional rights. However, Escobedo did request an attorney. Despite his repeated attempts, the lawyer was not permitted to see his client until police completed their interrogation.

Police testimony later revealed that Escobedo was handcuffed in a standing position and that he was agitated and upset. He spoke in Spanish to an officer who spoke his language, and during that conversation he revealed that he was aware of the shooting.

During the course of the police interrogation, Escobedo made incriminating statements that led to his indictment. Motions made before and during the trial to have these statements taken out of evidence were refused. After his conviction, the United States Supreme Court accepted the Escobedo case for review.

Constitutional Issue

The Court had to consider whether the Sixth Amendment's provision regarding right to counsel applied to the interrogation process.

The Court's Decision

The Court voted 5 to 4 to reverse Escobedo's conviction. Justice Arthur Goldberg wrote the Court's opinion. Goldberg determined that, although questioning had preceded formal indictment, it "should make no difference." At the point of interrogation, he stated, the investigation was no longer a "general investigation" of an unsolved crime. Escobedo "had become the accused, and the purpose of the investigation was to 'get him' to confess his guilt despite his

constitutional right not to do so," Goldberg maintained.

Justice Goldberg cited a number of previous cases in which having legal aid and advice early on had been crucial to the defendant. In the *Escobedo* case, the Court believed that legal advice during interrogation would have prevented Escobedo from making statements which virtually assured his conviction. Therefore, Goldberg stressed, to deny counsel during this early state made the trial "no more than an appeal from the interrogation."

Goldberg then replied to objections that the police would henceforth get fewer confessions because lawyers would automatically advise their clients to say nothing. Goldberg countered that this argument "cuts two ways," since it points out the critical importance, to the accused, of this stage in the judicial process. Goldberg continued, "There is necessarily a direct relationship between the importance of a stage to the police in their quest for a confession and the criticalness of that stage to the accused in his need for legal advice. Our Constitution . . . strikes the balance in favor of the right of the accused to be advised by his lawyer of his privilege against self-incrimination." In summarizing the Court's opinion, Goldberg noted that "when the investigation shifts from investigatory to accusatory—when its focus is on the accused and its purpose is to elicit a confession—our adversary system begins to operate, and . . . the accused must be permitted to consult with his lawyer."

Dissenting Opinions

Justice John M. Harlan wrote one of the four dissenting opinions in which he stated, "I think the rule announced today is most ill-conceived and that it seriously and unjustifiably fetters [restricts] perfectly legitimate methods of criminal law enforcement."

Justice Potter Stewart also dissented, agreeing with Harlan that the ruling gave advantages to the criminal and took away too much authority from law enforcers. He stated, in part, that this decision ". . . perverts those precious constitutional guarantees, and frustrates the vital interests of society in preserving the legitimate and proper function of honest and purposeful police investigation."

Analyzing the Case

1. At which point does the *Escobedo* decision rule that a lawyer must be provided?

_____

_____

_____

2. Which right of the accused does Justice Goldberg refer to as coming under the protection of the Constitution?

_____

_____

_____

3. In *Escobedo,* does the Court's decision protect a lawbreaker or a law enforcer? Support your position.

_____

_____

_____

Critical Thinking

4. **Demonstrating Reasoned Judgment** What is your opinion of the decision in this case? Explain your answer.

_____

_____

_____

_____

_____

_____

_____

_____

_____

_____

SUPREME COURT CASE   30

REYNOLDS V. SIMS (1964)

Background of the Case

Alabama was divided into voting districts for the state's Senate and House of Representatives. Each county, which represented one voting district, elected one senator, while the number of house members was based on population. As no reapportionment of voting districts had been made for 60 years, there was a vast discrepancy in the size of districts. The proportion of largest to smallest districts was about 41 to 1.

Two different reapportionment plans had passed the legislature. However, neither would result in a majority of the state's population being able to elect a majority of the legislators in either house.

A group of citizens and taxpayers sued to have the reapportionment plans declared unsatisfactory. A district court decision that had approved temporary use of one of the plans was appealed to the United States Supreme Court.

Constitutional Issue

Did the apportionment plans for the Alabama legislature violate the equal protection clause of the Fourteenth Amendment?

The Court's Decision

The Court ruled 8 to 1 that the equal protection clause had been violated. Chief Justice Earl Warren wrote for the Court.

In 1962 the Court had held in *Baker* v. *Carr* that voting districts must be substantially equal. The Court now had to decide whether the equal protection clause implied that both houses of a state legislature must also reflect equal numbers of people in a voting district. In other words, was it possible to elect a senate by weighted or unequally sized districts, using the United States Senate as an example?

Warren wrote that "legislators are elected by voters, not farms or citizens or economic interests." If voters in one area have votes whose numbers would have a disproportionately large impact in the election of representatives, then the votes of people in other areas become that much less effective. Warren stressed that "full and effective participation by all citizens in state government requires, therefore, that each citizen have an equally effective voice in the election of members of his state legislature." Otherwise his vote is debased and he is that much less a full citizen, explained Warren. This cannot depend on whether the voter resides in a sparsely populated rural district or a thickly populated urban area.

The Court rejected the analogy to the United States Senate. In the first place, the arrangement whereby each state gets an equal number of senators was "conceived out of compromise and concession indispensable to the founding of our federal republic." And, the Court stated, whereas the United States is a collection of independent and sovereign entities—states—the counties were never independent governments. Warren noted the national government was created by the states; the states were not created by the counties. They were and remain subordinate governments with no independent rights.

Following this reasoning, the Court said, "We hold that, as a basic constitutional standard, the equal protection clause requires that the seats in both houses of a bicameral state legislature must be apportioned on a population basis."

The precise arrangements for this requirement could vary. The two houses could represent different constituencies, be of different sizes, and be elected on different timetables for differing lengths of terms. All, however, must be worked out in lower courts, which will make adjustments according to local complexities.

This decision by the Court is often held, in abbreviated fashion, to have established the principle of "one person, one vote."

A Dissenting Opinion

As the only voice of dissent, Justice J. Harlan's objection was based on his opinion that state legislative apportionments are wholly free of constitutional limitations. He expressed the view that the Constitution only guaranteed that each state have a republican form of government and that the judiciary should not decide issues of individual state legislative apportionments.

Analyzing the Case

1. What decision did the United States Supreme Court have to make in the *Reynolds* v. *Sims* case?

_____

_____

_____

2. What effect would disproportionate numbers of votes in one area have on another area?

_____

_____

_____

3. Which argument by supporters of reapportionment in Alabama did the Supreme Court reject?

_____

_____

_____

Critical Thinking

4. **Determining Relevance** Of what significance is the "one person, one vote" principle in a democratic society?

_____

_____

_____

_____

_____

_____

_____

_____

_____

_____

SUPREME COURT CASE 31

WESBERRY V. SANDERS (1964)

Background of the Case

Like other congressional districts in Georgia, the Fifth District elected one representative. The Fifth District, however, had two to three times the population of other Georgia districts. Contending that this situation made his vote worth much less than the votes of some other Georgia citizens, Wesberry brought suit against Sanders, Georgia's governor. The suit asked that Sanders be prevented from holding elections under Georgia's statutes governing congressional district apportionment.

The federal district court which heard the case denied Wesberry's claim. It ruled that Wesberry's claim presented a nonjusticiable political question—that is, one which the court was powerless to decide. The case was then appealed to the United States Supreme Court.

Constitutional Issue

Wesberry's suit raised questions under various sections of the Fourteenth Amendment and under Article I, Section 2, of the Constitution. This article provides that "the House of Representatives shall be composed of members chosen . . . by the people of several states." The Court's decision was confined to a consideration of Article I and of *Baker* v. *Carr* (1962), in which the Court had ruled that voter district apportionment could be subject to judicial review.

The Court's Decision

Justice Hugo L. Black wrote for a 6 to 3 majority. The Court held that Georgia's districting statute did violate Article I, Section 2, of the Constitution. Since the federal district court had refused to intervene in what it held to be a political question, Black's first task was to review the *Baker* decision, which had stated that "the right to vote is too important in our free society to be stripped of judicial protection . . . on the ground of 'nonjusticiability.'"

Next, the Court announced that "in its historical context, the command of Article I, Section 2, . . . means that as nearly as is practicable one man's vote in a Congressional election is to be worth as much as another's." The remainder of the decision spells out the historical context.

Reviewing the debates of the Constitutional Convention, Black wrote that "it would defeat the principle embodied in the Great Compromise—equal representation in the House of equal numbers of people—for us to hold that, within the States, legislatures may draw the lines of congressional districts in such a way as to give some voters a greater voice in choosing a Congressman than others."

Black's review continued. He quoted James Madison, Charles Cotesworth Pinckney, and James Wilson, all to the effect that the Founders intended equally-sized congressional voting districts. So, in Wilson's words, "in this manner, the proportion of the representatives and of the constituents will remain invariably the same."

The Court's final conclusion was that "while it may not be possible to draw congressional districts with mathematical precision, that is no excuse for ignoring our Constitution's plain objective of making equal representation for equal numbers of people the fundamental goal for the House of Representatives. That is the high standard of justice and common sense which the Founders set for us."

A Dissenting Opinion

Justice John M. Harlan argued that (a) "congressional Representatives are to be apportioned among the several States largely, but not entirely, according to population"; (b) the states have power to choose "any method of popular election they please, subject only to the supervising power of Congress"; and (c) "the supervisory power of Congress is exclusive."

Above all, Harlan could find no justification for interpreting the phrase "by the people" in Article I, Section 2, as a requirement for equally proportioned voting districts. In support of his view, Harlan noted that all states, no matter how sparsely settled, are granted one representative in Congress, and that the three-fifths clause of Article I originally provided precisely for weighing some votes by three-fifths of the slave population. Harlan concluded: "The unstated premise of the Court's conclusion quite obviously is that the Congress has not dealt, and the Court believes it will not deal, with the problem of congressional apportionment in accordance with what the Court believes to be sound political principles. . . . The Court is not simply undertaking to exercise a power which the Constitution reserves to the Congress; it is also overruling congressional judgment. . . ."

Analyzing the Case

1. What prompted Wesberry's complaint?

_____

_____

_____

2. What does Justice Black say is the meaning of Article I, Section 2?

_____

_____

_____

3. On what grounds did Justice Harlan base his dissent?

_____

_____

_____

Critical Thinking

4. **Demonstrating Reasoned Judgment** Do you agree with the Court's decision? Why or why not?

_____

_____

_____

_____

_____

_____

_____

_____

SUPREME COURT CASE   32

MIRANDA V. ARIZONA (1966)

Background of the Case

The *Miranda* decision actually consolidated four cases dealing with substantially similar constitutional issues. In three state cases and one federal case, the persons involved had been convicted on the basis of confessions made after long periods of interrogation. None were informed of their right to counsel and to remain silent.

In the title case, Ernesto Miranda had been arrested at his Phoenix home and taken to the police station for questioning by two police officers. He was not advised of his right to an attorney or of his right to remain silent. After two hours of interrogation, he made and signed a written confession. He was subsequently found guilty of kidnapping and rape. He appealed the decision and the case was heard by the United States Supreme Court.

Constitutional Issue

Miranda's appeal to the United States Supreme Court was based on the Fifth Amendment's guarantee that "no person . . . shall be compelled in any criminal case to be a witness against himself." The Court took the case in order to further explore and clarify certain problems arising from earlier decisions related to the rights of individuals taken into police custody. The precise question in *Miranda* was: Under what circumstances may an interrogation take place that will produce a confession constitutionally admissible in a court of law?

The Court's Decision

The Supreme Court in a 5 to 4 vote overturned Miranda's conviction. Chief Justice Earl Warren wrote for the majority opinion.

The Court held that a prosecutor could use no statement "stemming from custodial interrogation of the defendant unless it demonstrates the use of procedural safeguards effective to secure the privilege against self-incrimination. By custodial interrogation, we mean questioning initiated by law enforcement officers after a person has been taken into custody or otherwise deprived of his freedom in any significant way."

Warren was highly concerned about what goes on in the "privacy" of interrogation. He observed that a suspect under interrogation is subjected to great psychological pressures designed "to put the defendant in such an emotional state as to impair his capacity for rational judgment. . . ." The Court's decision intended "to combat these pressures and to permit a full opportunity to exercise the privilege against self-incrimination. . . ."

In order that a suspect's rights be fully protected, Warren stated, "procedural safeguards must be employed." The Chief Justice explained, "He [the suspect] must be warned prior to any investigation that he has the right to remain silent, that anything he says may be used against him in a court of law, that he has the right to the presence of an attorney, and that, if he cannot afford an attorney, one will be appointed for him prior to any questioning if he so desires."

Once these warnings are given, the accused individual may choose to stop answering questions at any time, or he may halt an interrogation until his attorney is present. Otherwise, he may waive his exercise of these rights. In this instance, Warren warned, subsequently there would be "a heavy burden . . . on the Government to demonstrate that the defendant knowingly and intelligently waived his privilege against self-incrimination and his right to . . . counsel."

The Court held that such safeguards were "not intended to hamper the traditional function of police officers in investigating crime. . . ." The Court still permitted "general on-the-scene questioning as to facts surrounding a crime or other general questioning of citizens in the fact-finding process. . . . Volunteered statements of any kind are not barred by the Fifth Amendment." Warren stated, "There is no requirement that police stop a person who enters a police station and states that he wishes to confess to a crime, or a person who calls the police to offer a confession or any other statement he desires to make." Thus, the *Miranda* ruling only applies to interrogations.

Miranda is a landmark case that ensures that anyone held for interrogation must be clearly informed that he or she has the right to counsel and the right to have a lawyer present during the interrogation process. In addition, inability of an accused person to pay for a lawyer cannot be a reason for absence of counsel; a lawyer must be appointed to represent the accused regardless of the defendant's ability to pay.

Analyzing the Case

1. What does the Fifth Amendment guarantee?

_____

_____

_____

2. What did the Court mean by "custodial interrogation"?

_____

_____

_____

3. What kind of questioning does the *Miranda* decision allow?

_____

_____

_____

Critical Thinking

4. Demonstrating Reasoned Judgment "In the Court's zeal to protect the rights of the accused, those of the victim or the law enforcement officer often take second place." Do you agree or disagree with this statement? Give reasons for your answer.

_____

_____

_____

_____

_____

_____

_____

_____

_____

SUPREME COURT CASE   33

SHEPPARD V. MAXWELL (1966)

Background of the Case

Dr. Samuel Sheppard was accused of murdering his pregnant wife at their home in a Cleveland, Ohio, suburb on July 4, 1954. Sheppard claimed that the murderer had been an intruder, with whom he had fought and by whom he had been knocked unconscious.

Events prior to his indictment on August 12, 1954, were described as a "publicity circus." Such events included extensive, sensationalistic newspaper articles and editorials, containing allegations unfavorable to Sheppard, which never were brought up during the trial; a reenactment of the events of the crime, as Sheppard had told it, in front of police officials and news reporters; a proposal that Sheppard be questioned under "truth serum" drugs; and an inquest in a school auditorium, climaxed by Sheppard's lawyer's attempt to place some documents in evidence that were then being forcibly thrown out of the room by the coroner.

Furthermore, the trial began two weeks before the judge and the chief prosecutor were up for elective offices. The Cleveland newspapers published the names and addresses of the 75 people named as prospective jurors. They then received many letters and telephone calls concerning the case.

The courtroom was crammed with reporters, and the rest of the court building was largely given over to the media for telephone lines and broadcasting facilities. During the trial, witnesses, lawyers, and jurors were constantly photographed entering and leaving the courtroom. Reporters proved so noisy during the proceedings that the public-address system proved inadequate.

Information about deliberations, which were intended to remain secret from the jury, "leaked" and were printed in newspapers accessible to the jurors. Jurors were permitted, although not encouraged, to hear and read all kinds of pretrial and trial publicity, much of it damaging to Sheppard. They were also permitted to make telephone calls during recesses. The trial judge denied defense motions for a delay, to change the trial to another location, to declare a mistrial, and to question the jurors as to their exposure to publicity

Sheppard was convicted of second-degree murder. His appeals were all denied, and the United States Supreme Court declined to review the case.

Several years later he filed a petition for *habeas corpus* directed against the prison warden, E. L. Maxwell. *Habeas corpus* refers to an order that a prisoner be brought before a court to determine whether he or she has been denied due process. Sheppard's petition was granted and then denied by successive federal courts. He then appealed to the United States Supreme Court, which then accepted his case.

Constitutional Issue

Was Sheppard denied a fair trial, in violation of the due process clause of the Fourteenth Amendment?

The Court's Decision

The Court ruled for Sheppard in an 8 to 1 decision. Justice Tom S. Clark wrote for the Court.

He began by noting the historic importance of a free press in the administration of criminal justice. Clark stressed that "the press does not simply publish information about trials but guards against the miscarriage of justice by subjecting the police, prosecutors, and judicial processes to extensive public scrutiny and criticism.

At the same time, Clark explained, fair and orderly judicial administration requires that "the jury's verdict be based on evidence received in open court, not from outside sources." In the Sheppard case, the trial judge failed to control the manner of press coverage, to shield the jury from its onslaught, or to insulate witnesses from hearing each other's testimony.

Without forbidding press coverage, the judge might have taken actions such as preventing lawyers, witnesses, or court officials from discussing certain aspects of the case. He also could have requested city and county officials to regulate the dissemination of information by their employees. The press might also have been warned of the impropriety of publishing material that had not been part of the court proceedings. "Had the judge, the other officers of the court, and the police placed the interest of justice first, the news media would have soon learned to be content with the task of reporting the case as it unfolded in the courtroom—not pieced together from extra-judicial statements."

The Court concluded that due process had been violated in Sheppard's trial by the judge's failure "to protect Sheppard from the inherently prejudicial publicity which saturated the community and to control disruptive influences in the courtroom. . . ." Sheppard's *habeas corpus* petition was granted and his release ordered, although the state was given 60 days to order a new trial.

Analyzing the Case

1. What is a petition for *habeas corpus*?

_____

_____

_____

2. In what way had due process been violated in this case?

_____

_____

_____

Critical Thinking

3. **Identifying Alternatives** What would be some examples of actions the judge might have taken to ensure a fair trial?

_____

_____

_____

_____

_____

_____

_____

_____

_____

_____

Supreme Court Case   34

IN RE GAULT (1967)

Background of the Case

Gerald Gault, age 15, was taken into police custody with Ronald Lewis, a friend of his, on Monday, June 8, 1964. Neither of Gerald's parents were home at the time this police action was taken. The police left no notice at the home, and the parents were not notified that Gerald had been taken into custody and brought to a juvenile detention center.

The police action was taken on the basis of a neighbor's complaint that Gerald had made obscene remarks to her over the telephone. At that time, Gerald was serving a six-month probation for having been with another boy who had stolen a wallet.

After coming home and making inquiries, Gerald's mother learned that her son had been taken into custody. She went to the juvenile detention center at that time and was told that a hearing had been set for the next day. At that hearing, Gerald's accuser was not present and there was no formal statement about the facts surrounding the accusation. A petition had been requested by a deputy probation officer, but no notice of this petition was given to Gerald's family.

During the hearing, Gerald was questioned about the telephone call. Since no transcript of the hearing was made, the exact nature of the conversation at the hearing is not known. After this hearing, however, Gerald was sent back to the juvenile center and not released until June 12.

After a second hearing, again with the accusing neighbor absent and no transcript made, the judge committed Gerald to the State Industrial School until he reached age 21, unless released sooner by due process of law. Gerald did not have the same right to appeal this sentence that an adult would have had.

In fact, the maximum penalty under Arizona law for an adult who "in the pres-

ence or hearing of any woman or child . . . uses vulgar, abusive or obscene language" was $5 to $50, or imprisonment for not more than two months. The judge had also legally categorized Gerald as a "delinquent child" which, as the judge phrased it, was one who was "habitually involved in immoral matters."

This label seemed to be based on a few past instances, neither of which involved a hearing or a formal accusation. One instance involved Gerald stealing a baseball glove from another boy and lying to the police about it. Another instance involved Gerald making nuisance phone calls.

The Arizona Supreme Court upheld the decision of the lower court. The case then was heard by the United States Supreme Court.

Constitutional Issue

Had Gerald Gault been denied due process of law as guaranteed by the Fourteenth Amendment? Had he also been denied the right to counsel guaranteed by the Sixth Amendment and applied to the states through the Fourteenth Amendment?

The Court's Decision

Justice Abe Fortas wrote for the majority decision of the Court. The Court ruled 8 to 1 that due process had been denied to Gerald. In responding to the charge by the Gault family that Arizona's Juvenile Code, under which Gerald had been sentenced, was unconstitutional, the Court ruled that the following basic rights were denied in this case: (1) the right to receive notice of the charges; (2) the right to counsel; (3) the right to confrontation and cross-examination; (4) privilege against self-incrimination; (5) the right to a transcript of the proceedings; and (6) the right to appellate review. In this case the Court found that Gerald had not been informed of his constitutional rights including the right to counsel. He had not been given sufficient, written notice of either the charges against him or the hearings in enough time to prepare an adequate defense. Further, unsworn hearsay testimony was used against Gerald, and the neighbor never appeared to answer questions or confirm her charges at the hearings.

Fortas rejected the finding of the lower courts that the probation officer and the parent provided sufficient protection for the rights of a juvenile. He wrote, "The probation officer cannot act as counsel for the child. . . . Nor can the judge represent the child. A proceeding where the issue is whether the child will be found 'delinquent' and subjected to the loss of his liberty . . . is comparable in seriousness to a felony prosecution. The juvenile needs the assistance of counsel to cope with problems of law." Gerald and his parents, then, should have been notified of the right to counsel and had one appointed for them if they could not afford to hire their own lawyer.

The Court also found that there was an absence of a valid confession and that sworn testimony by witnesses who would also be available for cross-examination was required, but not existing, in this case. All of these factors would have been necessary to find a 15-year-old boy "delinquent" and commit him to a state institution.

Analyzing the Case

1. List the basic rights that were denied to Gerald Gault in this case.

_____

_____

_____

2. What circumstances during the two hearings violated Gerald's rights?

_____

_____

_____

Critical Thinking

3. Demonstrating Reasoned Judgment Do you think that juveniles should have any special privileges before the law that adults do not have, such as private trials and nondisclosure of their names?

_____

_____

_____

_____

_____

_____

_____

_____

_____

SUPREME COURT CASE   35

KATZ V. UNITED STATES (1967)

Background of the Case

While gathering evidence for the prosecution of Charles Katz, the Federal Bureau of Investigation (FBI) "bugged" a telephone booth by attaching a microphone and tape recorder to the outside of the booth. This action was taken without a warrant. Based on the evidence that resulted, Katz was tried and convicted in California for using telephone lines to transmit betting information from Los Angeles to Miami and Boston. This action violated federal communications statutes.

Katz appealed his conviction on the grounds that a public telephone is a constitutionally protected area. He thus argued that evidence obtained by attaching an electronic listening device to a phone booth is obtained in violation of the right to privacy of the person using the booth.

Constitutional Issue

Katz claimed that his right to privacy, a right which the Court previously inferred from the Fourth Amendment's protection against unreasonable search and seizure, had been violated. The government, relying on rulings that had held electronic eavesdropping legal when no trespass was involved, claimed that the FBI wiretap was legal because it was on the outside of the booth.

The Court's Decision

The Court decided 7 to 1 against the government. Justice Stewart wrote for the Court.

Although the government and Katz had both argued mostly over whether a phone booth was "a constitutionally protected area," the Court's decision followed a slightly different path, stating that "the Fourth Amendment protects people, not places." Therefore, the government's argument of not actually penetrating the phone booth was found to be beside the point. Stewart

declared that "a person in a phone booth may rely upon the protection of the Fourth Amendment [and] is surely entitled to assume that the words he utters into the mouthpiece will not be broadcast to the world." Given this reasoning, he continued, "it becomes clear that the reach of that Amendment cannot turn upon the presence or absence of a physical intrusion into any given enclosure."

Since Katz had "justifiably relied" on his privacy while using the phone booth, the government's violation of that privacy constituted a search and seizure in violation of the Fourth Amendment. In addition, the Court pointed out that the very "narrowly circumscribed" surveillance involved here could well have been authorized by a warrant. Not to have done so ignored the central element of the Fourth Amendment, that is, justification before the fact and not afterward.

In making this point, Stewart wrote, "The government stresses the fact that the telephone booth . . . was made partly of glass, so that he [Katz] was as visible after he entered it as he would have been if he had remained outside. But what he sought to exclude when he entered the booth was not the intruding eye—it was the uninvited ear. He did not shed his right to do so simply because he made his calls from a place where he might be seen. No less than an individual in a business office, in a friend's apartment, or in a taxicab, a person in a telephone booth may rely upon the protection of the Fourth Amendment. . . . To read the Constitution more narrowly is to ignore the vital role that the public telephone has come to play in private communication."

In concurring, Justice John M. Harlan developed a test for determining what interests are protected: "First that a person has exhibited an actual (subjective) expectation of privacy, and second, that the expectation be one that society is prepared to recognize as 'reasonable.'" This test became an accepted standard.

A Dissenting Opinion

As the only voice of dissent in this case, Justice Black expressed the opinion that eavesdropping using electronic means did not constitute "search and seizure." He thought that the words of the Fourth Amendment quite literally only applied to "tangible things with size, form, and weight." He was referring, of course, to the phrasing of the Fourth Amendment that people had the right "to be secure in their persons, houses, papers, and effects, against unreasonable searches and seizures. . . ."

In concluding his remarks, Black wrote, "The Court talks about a constitutional 'right of privacy' as though there is some constitutional provision or provisions forbidding any law ever to be passed which might abridge the 'privacy' of individuals. But there is not."

Analyzing the Case

1. Why did the FBI think its surveillance was legal?

_____

_____

_____

2. How did the Court's approach differ from that of Katz and the government?

_____

_____

_____

Critical Thinking

3. **Predicting Consequences** Could the FBI legally have recorded Katz's conversations?

_____

_____

_____

_____

_____

_____

_____

_____

_____

_____

_____

_____

SUPREME COURT CASE 36

GREGORY V. CHICAGO (1969)

Background of the Case

Dick Gregory, a comic and civil rights activist, helped lead a protest against the slow pace at which Chicago's public schools were being desegregated. A march was organized. It began at Chicago's City Hall and ended at Mayor Richard Daley's house, about five miles away.

The mayor's neighborhood of Bridgeport was an all-white area with a history of hostility to African Americans. A hostile neighborhood crowd soon gathered, attempting in various ways to harass the largely African American protesters. They, in turn, were under strict orders by march leaders to remain orderly and nonviolent. Over several hours the neighborhood crowd grew from about 150 to more than 1,000 people.

Police made vigilant efforts to control the crowd, which had become increasingly violent, hurling racial abuse, eggs, and rocks. Finally the police made repeated requests that Gregory lead the marchers out of the neighborhood. Three marchers accepted the offer of a police escort from the area. Those remaining, Gregory included, were then arrested and removed in police vans. He and others were convicted later for disorderly conduct.

The Supreme Court of Illinois upheld the convictions. The Illinois Court suggested that the demonstrators had been arrested not so much for marching but for refusing to obey the police request to disperse. An appeal from this decision was lodged with the United States Supreme Court.

Constitutional Issue

Were the marchers' First Amendment rights to free speech and assembly, as applied to states by the due process clause of the Fourteenth Amendment, violated in this instance?

The Court's Decision

The Court ruled unanimously that the defendants had been deprived of their First Amendment rights. Chief Justice Earl Warren wrote for the Court.

Warren declared that "this is a simple case." He added, "Petitioners' march, if peaceful and orderly, falls well within the sphere of conduct protected by the First Amendment." As there was no evidence that the marchers had been disorderly, their conduct was legal.

He responded likewise to the suggestion of the Illinois Supreme Court that the conviction was actually for refusing to obey a police officer. The Chief Justice stated, "However reasonable the police request may have been and however laudable the police motives, petitioners were charged and convicted for holding a demonstration, not for refusal to obey a police officer." He continued, quoting a former Court decision in *Garner* v. *Louisiana,* "It is as much a denial of due process to send an accused to prison following conviction for a charge that was never made as it is to convict him upon a charge for which there is no evidence to support that conviction."

Warren went on to applaud the efforts of both the police and Gregory's marchers to maintain peace and order under the most trying circumstances. He went over more specifics of the case that gave even more credence to the fact that Gregory and his group of marchers had maintained a peaceful attitude in the face of an angry mob. They had been told to stop singing at 8:30 that evening and they had done so. In spite of the fact that the hostile crowd threw rocks and other objects at them, the marchers did not engage in any acts of violence toward the crowd. Warren wrote, "Indeed, in the face of jeers, insults, and assaults with rocks and eggs, Gregory and his group maintained a decorum that speaks well of their determination simply to tell their side of their grievances and complaints." Doing so, the Court concluded, was all within their First Amendment rights.

In a separate opinion, Justice Hugo Black concurred in greater detail. He found the disorderly conduct law itself to be unconstitutionally vague. He argued that a properly drawn statute could constitutionally protect both public order and demonstrators' First Amendment rights, "but under our democratic system of government, law-making is not entrusted to the moment-to-moment judgment of the policeman on his beat. . . . To let a policeman's command become equivalent to a criminal statute comes dangerously near to making our government one of men rather than of laws."

Analyzing the Case

1. What reason did the Illinois Supreme Court give for its decision?

_____

_____

_____

2. Why did Warren rule in favor of the demonstrators?

_____

_____

_____

3. What was Black's main objection to the disorderly conduct statute?

_____

_____

_____

Critical Thinking

4. **Making Comparisons** What difference is there between Warren's and Black's conclusions about the Gregory case?

_____

_____

_____

_____

_____

_____

_____

_____

SUPREME COURT CASE   37

TINKER V. DES MOINES SCHOOL DISTRICT (1969)

Background of the Case

John Tinker and Christopher Eckhardt were high school students in Des Moines, Iowa. Along with John's sister, Mary Beth, a junior high school student, they were involved in planning a protest against U.S. involvement in Vietnam. In December 1965, along with their parents and others, the trio met to consider ways to publicize their protest. They decided that on December 16 and on New Year's Eve they would wear a black armband in order to indicate their support for a truce.

School authorities learned of these plans and on December 14 announced that any student wearing an armband would be asked to remove it or be suspended. Mary Beth and Christopher wore their armbands to school on December 16. John wore his the following day. All were suspended. The fathers of the students then filed a complaint in the United States District Court for the Southern District of Iowa seeking an injunction against the disciplinary action of the school authorities; they also sought nominal damages.

In the legal actions that followed, the district court sided with school authorities. The decision was upheld by an appeals court. The case then went on appeal to the United States Supreme Court.

Constitutional Issue

Was the wearing of armbands as a political protest in the public schools protected by the First Amendment's guarantee of freedom of speech?

The Court's Decision

The Court held 7 to 2 that this form of expression was protected by the First Amendment. Justice Abe Fortas wrote for the Court.

On the one hand, Justice Fortas observed, "It can hardly be argued that either students or teachers shed their constitutional rights to freedom of speech or expression at the schoolhouse gate. . . . On the other hand, the Court has repeatedly emphasized the need for affirming the comprehensive authority of the States and of school officials, consistent with fundamental constitutional safeguards, to prescribe and control conduct in the schools. . . ."

The Court found that there had been no evidence of any interference with the rights of other students or any disruption of classes. Yet the district court had supported school authorities because their fear of a potential disturbance was reasonable. The Court took note of this possibility but stated that "our Constitution says we must take this risk."

The Court also found it relevant that no general prohibition existed against wearing any controversial or political symbol, only black armbands. Such selective prohibition was held to be unconstitutional. Fortas went on to write, "If a regulation were adopted by school officials forbidding discussion of the Vietnam conflict, or the expression by any student of opposition to it anywhere on school property except as part of a prescribed classroom exercise, it would be obvious that the regulation would violate the constitutional rights of students, at least if it could not be justified by a showing that the students' activities would materially and substantially disrupt the work and the discipline of the school."

Students, whether in or out of school, were held to be "persons" under the Constitution, according to Justice Fortas. They have fundamental rights that must be respected. He emphasized, "In our system, students may not be regarded as closed-circuit recipients of only that which the State chooses to communicate. They may not be confined to the expression of those sentiments that are officially approved."

The Court's ruling concluded that "the wearing of armbands in the circumstances of this case was entirely divorced from actually or potentially disruptive conduct by those participating in it. It was closely akin to 'pure speech' which, we have repeatedly held, is entitled to comprehensive protection under the First Amendment."

A Dissenting Opinion

Justice Hugo Black wrote a dissenting opinion. He felt that the state's elected school officials and not the courts should have the right to decide which school disciplinary actions are "reasonable." He felt that there was evidence that the wearing of the armbands and all the controversy that surrounded that action did, in fact, disrupt school routine and classwork. Overall, he felt that the Court's decision gave too much power to the students and took away too much authority from the states and the school authorities.

Analyzing the Case

1. Whose interests were in conflict in the *Tinker* case?

_____

_____

_____

2. In what circumstances is the right of free expression in schools not absolute?

_____

_____

_____

Critical Thinking

3. **Recognizing Ideologies** What does it mean to be a "person" under the Constitution?

_____

_____

_____

_____

_____

_____

_____

_____

_____

_____

_____

SUPREME COURT CASE 38

NEW YORK TIMES CO. V. UNITED STATES (1971)

Background of the Case

Involvement of United States troops in an undeclared war in Vietnam had given rise to a great deal of public protest in the late 1960s and early 1970s. Among those opposing the war was Daniel Ellsberg, a political scientist working for the Pentagon. In 1971 Ellsberg stole and copied a lengthy classified paper entitled "History of United States Decision-Making Process of Vietnam Policy," often referred to as "The Pentagon Papers." Ellsberg turned these documents over to *The New York Times*, which began to publish them on June 13, 1971.

On June 15, the federal government sought, and was granted, a temporary order stopping the *Times* from publishing the papers. With uncharacteristic speed the case was appealed through to the United States Supreme Court within the next 10 days. The case was heard almost immediately and the decision made on June 30, 1971.

Constitutional Issue

The First Amendment, as applied to the states through the due process clause of the Fourteenth Amendment, guarantees the freedoms of speech and of the press. The question in this case was whether, in the absence of any statute authorizing such action, the government could prevent the publication of materials on the ground that the national security was endangered.

The Court's Decision

The Court's decision was issued *per curiam*, which means that it is issued by the Court as a whole. The justice writing the decision is not identified. Along with the *per curiam* decision that there could be no prior restraint on the press in this instance, all nine justices wrote separate opinions. Six justices concurred, and three dissented. The *per curiam* opinion was quite brief. It cited sev-

eral earlier cases to the effect that "any system of prior restraints of expression comes to this Court bearing a heavy presumption against its constitutional validity." The Court ruled that the government had not met this burden.

Justice Hugo L. Black wrote that the Court should not even have heard oral argument in the case, and the government's injunction should have been automatically denied. "In my view, it is unfortunate that some of my Brethren are willing to hold that the publication of news may sometimes be enjoined. Such a holding would make a shambles of the First Amendment. . . ." Black's view of the First Amendment was that "the press was protected so that it could bare the secrets of government and inform the people." In his opinion, the newspapers which published these papers "should be commended."

Justice William O. Douglas agreed, and noted that there was no statute barring the press from publishing such material. In fact, an earlier version of a law on which the government had relied to make its case had been specifically intended to enable the President to stop the press from publishing material deemed harmful during a "national emergency." That provision had been rejected by the Congress.

Justice William J. Brennan also concurred. In his opinion, the original injunction should have been denied unless the government had been prepared to demonstrate inevitable, direct, and immediate harm. Even a temporary order barring publication long enough for a court to examine such a claim would, in his view, violate the First Amendment.

Justice Potter Stewart agreed that sometimes secrecy in government is necessary, but it is entirely up to the executive branch to protect its secrets. "The responsibility must be where the power is," he observed.

Stewart was "convinced that the Executive is correct with regard to some of the documents involved." Even so, he could not say that "disclosure of any of them will surely result in direct, immediate, and irreparable damage to our Nation or its people. That being so, there can under the First Amendment be but one judicial resolution of the issues before us."

Dissenting Opinions

Chief Justice Warren Burger dissented. He viewed the case as a headlong collision between two imperatives, "a free and unfettered press" and "the effective functioning of a complex modern government." Since he rejected the view that the First Amendment grants "absolute" privileges to the press, Burger wished for adequate time in which to consider the competing claims of press and government.

Justice Harry A. Blackmun dissented too. He also argued that time pressures in the case had been too limiting to arrive at a reasoned judgment. He expressed concern that the publication of the Pentagon papers would lead to battlefield casualties and diplomatic difficulties.

Analyzing the Case

1. What was the *per curiam* conclusion made in the *Times* case?

_____

_____

_____

2. What was the basis of the position taken by Justice Douglas?

_____

_____

_____

Critical Thinking

3. **Drawing Conclusions** The *Times* case advanced through several levels of the state and federal judicial system in record time. What reason(s) justified such speed in your opinion?

_____

_____

_____

_____

_____

_____

_____

_____

_____

_____

_____

SUPREME COURT CASE　　39

MILLER V. CALIFORNIA (1973)

Background of the Case

Miller had sent out large, unrequested mailings to advertise so-called adult books and films. The brochures contained sexually explicit photographs and drawings. His conviction was specifically based on his conduct in causing five unsolicited advertising brochures to be sent through the mail in an envelope addressed to a restaurant in Newport Beach, California. The manager and his mother opened the envelope and complained to the police.

Miller was prosecuted under California's obscenity laws. The jury was instructed by the judge to evaluate the materials by the contemporary community standards of California. The court found him guilty on several legal counts. Eventually, the United States Supreme Court heard the case.

Constitutional Issue

Miller's appeal involved local interpretations of obscenity and state actions. Can a state, under the First Amendment guarantees of free speech and a free press, prosecute publishers of materials considered "obscene" by local authorities?

The Court's Decision

The Court voted 5 to 4 in California's favor. Chief Justice Warren Burger wrote the majority opinion.

Relying on earlier decisions, the Court affirmed that "states have a legitimate interest in prohibiting dissemination or exhibition of obscene material." However, this holds true only when there is "a significant danger of offending the sensibilities of unwilling recipients or of exposure to juveniles." Earlier standards required prosecutors to prove that material is "utterly without redeeming social value." Burger rejected this principle and sought new standards in "an area in which there are few eternal verities."

Therefore, the Court proposed three guidelines for new statutes regulating offensive material. First, would the average person, "applying contemporary community standards," find that a work, when viewed as a whole, appealed to "prurient interest"? Second, does the work depict or describe certain specifically defined sexual conduct in a patently offensive way? Finally, taken as a whole, does the work lack "serious literary, artistic, political, or scientific value"?

Burger described these standards as prohibiting except in those instances where materials "depict or describe patently offensive 'hard core' sexual conduct specifically defined by the regulating state law. . . ."

Finally, Burger defended the decision to leave the determination of actual tests to local powers. "Under a national Constitution, fundamental First Amendment limitations on the powers of states do not vary. . . ." Nonetheless, "It is neither realistic nor constitutionally sound to read the First Amendment as requiring that the people of Maine or Mississippi accept public depiction of conduct found tolerable in Las Vegas or New York City. . . . People in different states vary in their tastes and attitudes, and this diversity is not to be strangled by the absolutism of imposed uniformity. . . ."

A Dissenting Opinion

Justice William O. Douglas wrote a dissenting opinion in which he criticized the Court for its history of indecision regarding exactly what constituted "obscene material." Regarding the new criteria that the Court devised to judge obscenity, he wrote, "Yet how under these vague tests can we sustain convictions for the sale of an article prior to the time when some court has declared it to be obscene?"

Douglas made many references to the fact that only a constitutional amendment could firmly define what would be considered obscene. He expressed this thought, in part, "What shocks me may be sustenance for my neighbor. . . . We deal here with a regime of censorship which, if adopted, should be done by constitutional amendment after full debate by the people." He continued, "I do not think we, the judges, were ever given the constitutional power to make definitions of obscenity. If it is to be defined, let the people debate it and decide by a constitutional amendment what they want to ban as obscene and what standards they want the legislatures and the courts to apply." He complained that the use of the general term "'offensive'. . . gives authority to government that cuts the very vitals out of the First Amendment."

Analyzing the Case

1. What new guidelines did Chief Justice Warren Burger suggest for statutes regulating offensive material?

_____

_____

_____

2. How would you describe the apparent conflict between a community's interpretation of obscenity and the application of principles contained in the First Amendment?

_____

_____

_____

3. Describe the basis for the dissent by Justice Douglas.

_____

_____

_____

Critical Thinking

4. **Evaluating Information** Does "free" speech or "free" press mean that persons or the materials that they produce should be allowed to exist with no regulation or restrictions? Explain.

_____

_____

_____

_____

_____

_____

_____

_____

_____

_____

SUPREME COURT CASE 40

ROE V. WADE (1973)

Background of the Case

Jane Roe (a pseudonym) was an unmarried pregnant woman who brought suit against District Attorney Wade of Dallas County, Texas. Roe's suit challenged a Texas statute prohibiting abortions except when, in a doctor's judgment, abortion would be necessary to save the mother's life. Since Roe's life was not endangered by her pregnancy, she had not been able to obtain an abortion in Texas.

Constitutional Issue

Roe argued that the protection of life granted by the Fourteenth Amendment could not be applied to a fetus because a fetus was not a person in the eyes of the law. She also argued that her decision to obtain an abortion should be protected by the right of privacy, a right which stemmed from the Bill of Rights generally and from the liberty guaranteed by the Fourteenth Amendment.

The Court's Decision

In a 7 to 2 vote, the Court decided in Roe's favor on both points, although with some qualifications. Justice Harry A. Blackmun wrote for the Court.

The Court approached its decision by acknowledging the delicacy and depth of the issue before it. Nevertheless, it was the Court's task "to resolve the issue by constitutional measurement free of emotion and of predilection."

Justice Blackmun reaffirmed that there was a right to privacy that could be inferred from the First, Fourth, Fifth, Ninth, and Fourteenth Amendments. He said that "the right has some extension to activities relating to marriage . . . , procreation . . . , (and) contraception. . . ." Accordingly, "the right of privacy . . . is broad enough to encompass a woman's decision whether or not to terminate her pregnancy," he concluded. Although specific and direct medical injury might follow a denial of choice, other injuries as well could result from an unwanted pregnancy. These include "a distressful life and future, psychological harm, and also the distress . . . associated with the unwanted child, and . . . the problem of bringing a child into a family already unable, psychologically and otherwise, to care for it." Yet the Court granted no absolute right to an abortion, as that decision "must be considered against important state interests in regulation. . . ."

The Court's discussion then turned to the question of fetal personhood. Although Wade had argued that a fetus was a person, he conceded that there was no case to be cited in support of his position. The Court, too, was persuaded that "the word *person*, as used in the Fourteenth Amendment, does not include the unborn. . . . On this point, Blackmun explained, "The law has been reluctant to endorse any theory that life, as we recognize it, begins before live birth or to accord legal rights to the unborn except in narrowly defined situations and except when the rights are contingent upon live birth." The state, in fact, was held to have two separate and distinct interests. According to the Court, one is "preserving and protecting the health of the pregnant woman" and the other is "in protecting the potentiality of human life."

To satisfy both sets of interests and rights, the Court divided the term of pregnancy into two parts, based on "present medical knowledge." The first part is the first trimester, or three-month period of pregnancy. This period was identified as the point up to which fewer women died from abortions than in normal childbirth. In order to preserve and protect women during this period, a state may regulate abortion procedures in such areas as doctors' qualifications and licensing of facilities. Up to this point, however, the state may not regulate a doctor's medical determination that a pregnancy should be terminated.

The point at which the state's compelling interest in preserving potential life begins is when that life is viable, or capable of living outside the womb. During this period the state may constitutionally forbid abortion, except when necessary to preserve a woman's life or health. Between the end of the first trimester and the beginning of the period of viability—not specified, but usually the second trimester—the state may "if it chooses, regulate the abortion procedure in ways that are reasonably related to maternal health," the Court concluded.

A Dissenting Opinion

In his dissent, Justice William H. Rehnquist debated whether any constitutional right to privacy could be so broad as to include the complete restriction of state controls on abortion during the first trimester. In this regard, he wrote, "There apparently was no question concerning the validity of this provision or of any of the other state statutes when the Fourteenth Amendment was adopted. The only conclusion possible from this history is that the drafters did not intend to have the Fourteenth Amendment withdraw from the States the power to legislate with respect to this matter. . . ."

Analyzing the Case

1. What is the constitutional origin of the right to privacy?

_____

_____

_____

2. What dual interest does the state have here?

_____

_____

_____

Critical Thinking

3. **Recognizing Ideologies** Up to what point has a woman an unquestioned right to an abortion?

_____

_____

_____

_____

_____

_____

_____

_____

_____

SUPREME COURT CASE 41

LAU V. NICHOLS (1974)

Background of the Case

Approximately 2,856 non-English-speaking students of Chinese ancestry were enrolled in San Francisco public schools in the early 1970s. Of this number, about 1,000 received some form of supplemental help in English through programs in the San Francisco Unified School District. The rest of these students apparently were unable to receive any similar aid. On their behalf Kinney Kinmon Lau filed a lawsuit through his guardian, Mrs. Kam Wai Lau, in the federal district court.

The suit sought to force officials to provide English-language help for those Chinese-speaking students requiring it. The nature of the aid expected was not specified. Lau maintained only that unequal educational opportunities were currently available to Chinese-speaking students.

The district court denied Lau's petition. A federal appeals court upheld the district court's ruling. The case then went to the United States Supreme Court.

Constitutional Issue

The Laus claimed that their rights under the equal protection clause of the Fourteenth Amendment were being denied. They also argued that they were entitled to assistance under the 1964 Civil Rights Act, which prohibited recipients of federal funds from discrimination against individuals on the basis of race, color, or national origin.

The Court's Decision

The Court decided unanimously in favor of the Laus. Justice William O. Douglas wrote for the Court.

The Court declined to address the constitutional issues raised in the case. Their decision was based entirely on the Civil Rights Act and its administrative regulations. Said Douglas, "Basic English skills are at the very core of what these public schools teach. Imposition of a requirement that, before a child can effectively participate in the educational program, he must already have acquired those basic skills is to make a mockery of public education."

Under United States Department of Health, Education and Welfare (now the Department of Health and Human Services and the Department of Education) regulations governing the administration of the Civil Rights Act, recipients of federal funds, such as a school district, were forbidden to provide unequal services or benefits or unequal advantages. Moreover, "discrimination is barred which has that effect even though no purposeful design is present," he stated.

To the Court it was "obvious the Chinese-speaking minority receives fewer benefits than the English-speaking majority . . . which denies them a meaningful opportunity to participate in the educational program." The Court ordered the schools to "take affirmative steps to rectify the language deficiency in order to open its instructional program to these students."

Justice P. Stewart added this to the discussion in this case: "The interpretive guidelines published by the Office for Civil Rights of the Department of Health, Education, and Welfare in 1970 clearly indicate that affirmative efforts to give special training for non-English-speaking pupils are required by Title VI as a condition to receipt of federal aid to public schools." He quotes Title VI as stating, "Where inability to speak and understand the English language excludes national origin-minority group children from effective participation in the educational program offered by a school district, the school district must take affirmative steps to rectify the language deficiency in order to open its instructional program to these students."

Justice Harry Blackmun agreed with the Court's ruling. However, he stated that if the case concerned only a few children or a single child, he would not feel compelled to reach the same result. He wrote, "Against the possibility that the Court's judgment may be interpreted too broadly, I stress the fact that the children with whom we are concerned here number about 1,800. This is a very substantial group that is being deprived of any meaningful schooling because the children cannot understand the language of the classroom. . . . I merely wish to make plain that when, in another case, we are concerned with a very few youngsters, . . . I would not regard today's decision . . . as conclusive upon the issue whether the statute and guidelines require the funded school district to provide special instruction. For me, numbers are at the very heart of this case and my concurrence is to be understood accordingly."

Analyzing the Case

1. What constitutional grounds determined the decision in this case?

_____

_____

_____

2. What did Douglas call a "mockery"?

_____

_____

_____

Critical Thinking

3. **Demonstrating Reasoned Judgment** Do you think Justice Blackmun's qualifications about the size of the student population to be served pose any problems? Explain your answer.

_____

_____

_____

_____

_____

_____

_____

_____

_____

_____

_____

_____

SUPREME COURT CASE   42

UNITED STATES V. NIXON (1974)

Background of the Case

During President Richard M. Nixon's 1974 reelection campaign, burglars broke into the Democratic National Committee's headquarters in the Watergate office and apartment complex in Washington, D.C. Alleged ties between some of the burglars and the Committee to Reelect the President caused a nationwide public and political outcry. As a result of events involving federal appointees and others, the United States Department of Justice appointed a special prosecutor to carry out an independent investigation of what became known as the Watergate scandal.

The investigation and subsequent trials revealed, among other things, that the President had taped many conversations in the White House's Oval Office. Leon Jaworski, the special prosecutor, attempted to subpoena the tapes. [A *subpoena* is a legal paper demanding that persons or evidence be brought before a court.]

The President refused to surrender the tapes. He claimed executive privilege, which protects the Office of the President from being compelled by the judicial branch to turn over confidential executive branch material. Because the tapes were needed for a trial scheduled to begin shortly, the United States Supreme Court agreed to hear the case immediately without requiring that the case follow a normal appeals route.

Constitutional Issue

Could the President claim executive privilege in refusing to surrender material to a federal court?

The Court's Decision

The Court agreed unanimously that the President had to turn over the tapes. Chief Justice Warren Burger wrote for the Court. The extraordinary grant of authority to the

special prosecutor, wrote Justice Burger, "gives the special prosecutor explicit power to contest the invocation of executive privilege in the process of seeking evidence deemed relevant. . . ."

The Court next ruled that it was competent to decide the case, just as it had decided similar controversies between officers and branches of government in the past. In addition, since the material was wanted for a normal federal criminal trial, the matter fell directly under the Court's jurisdiction through the judicial powers spelled out in Article III of the Constitution.

The Chief Justice now turned his attention to the claim of executive privilege. The President claimed that executive privilege was secure from a subpoena for two reasons. First, it was necessary to protect the confidentiality of high-level communications. Second, the principle of separation of powers protects the President through the independence of the executive branch.

The Court found this argument insufficient, depending on merely a broad and undifferentiated claim of public interest that such conversations remain confidential. It might have been different if this had been a claim to protect "military, diplomatic or sensitive national security secrets . . . ," the Court stated.

Burger further reasoned that this claim based on the separation of powers would work to impair the balance of those powers. He wrote: "To read the Article II powers of the President as providing an absolute privilege as against a subpoena essential to enforcement of criminal statutes on no more than a generalized claim of the public interest in the confidentiality of nonmilitary and nondiplomatic discussions would upset the constitutional balance of a 'workable government' and gravely impair the role of the courts under Article III." Against the

President's claim of executive privilege stood the Sixth Amendment rights of an accused to subpoena evidence and the Fifth Amendment guarantees against being deprived of liberty without due process of law. The Court weighed these claims and concluded that "without access to specific facts a criminal prosecution may be totally frustrated. The President's broad interest in confidentiality . . . will not be vitiated by disclosure of a limited number of conversations preliminarily shown to have some bearing on the pending criminal cases." In short, the Court concluded, the President's claim "cannot prevail over the fundamental demands of due process of law in the fair administration of criminal justice."

Finally, the Court ordered certain safeguards on the handling of this material while in the possession of the district court. These safeguards included that it would be examined by the judge in private; only relevant material would be used; confidentiality would be preserved as far as was possible; and the material would be safely returned.

Analyzing the Case

1. Under what circumstances might executive privilege have been properly asserted?

_____

_____

_____

2. What reasons did the President feel justified his claim of executive privilege?

_____

_____

_____

Critical Thinking

3. Identifying Central Ideas What rights did the Court see as being in opposition to the President's claim?

_____

_____

_____

_____

_____

_____

_____

_____

_____

_____

SUPREME COURT CASE   43

GREGG V. GEORGIA (1976)

Background of the Case

Troy Leon Gregg and Floyd Allen, two hitchhikers, were picked up in Florida by Fred Simmons and Bob Moore. The following day the bodies of Moore and Simmons were discovered in a ditch near a rest stop. They had both been shot.

Following a description provided by a third hitchhiker who had been in the car for part of the journey, police found and arrested Gregg and Allen in North Carolina, who were driving Simmons' car. The 0.25-caliber pistol used in the slayings was found in Gregg's pocket.

Allen claimed in statements to police that Gregg had intended to rob the two men all along, and that he had done so after killing them. Gregg claimed that he had fired in self-defense when he and Allen had been attacked by Moore and Simmons.

The judge submitted the case to the jury with instructions on felony murder, non-felony murder, and self-defense. The jury found Gregg guilty of armed robbery and murder.

In Georgia, murder and armed robbery convictions were given presentencing hearings during which a jury would hear any "evidence in extenuation, mitigation, and aggravation of punishment . . . ," including previous criminal record or its absence. At least one of ten specified aggravating circumstances had to be present in order to impose a death penalty.

If the sentence was death, an appeals process was provided for, including expedited appeal to the Georgia Supreme Court. That Court had to consider whether the death penalty had been imposed "under the influence of passion, prejudice or any other arbitrary factor," and whether the sentence was "excessive or disproportionate to the penalty imposed in similar cases, considering both the crime and the defendant."

The Georgia Supreme Court upheld Gregg's death sentence for murder, but not for armed robbery. Gregg appealed to the United States Supreme Court.

Constitutional Issue

Did the Georgia death penalty statute amount to "cruel and unusual punishment" under the Eighth and Fourteenth Amendments?

The Court's Decision

The Court upheld Georgia's statute by a 7 to 2 vote, although a majority could not agree on any one opinion. Six justices agreed that the death penalty does not, in all circumstances, constitute cruel and unusual punishment. They also agreed that a state's statutes are not unconstitutional simply because the prosecution had the discretion to choose whether to plea-bargain or seek conviction on a capital charge.

Justice Potter Stewart announced the Court's decision, joined by two other Justices. Stewart wrote: "American draftsmen, who adopted the English phrasing in drafting the Eighth Amendment, were primarily concerned with proscribing 'tortures' and other 'barbarous' methods of punishment." They did not, however, place the death penalty in these categories. Early Court decisions agreed; "the constitutionality of the sentence of death itself was not at issue. . . ." In fact, Stewart observed, the death penalty has long been accepted under United States law, and "it is apparent from the text of the Constitution itself that the existence of capital punishment was accepted by the Framers."

A death penalty conviction must, however, meet certain criteria. It must accord with "the dignity of man," which is the "basic concept" of the Eighth Amendment, Stewart wrote. It must not be "excessive." He continued: "First, the punishment must not involve the unnecessary and wanton infliction of pain. . . . Second, the punishment must not be grossly out of proportion to the severity of the crime." Whatever may be true of evolving standards of decency and changing sentiments on the contemporary appropriateness of a death penalty, it still serves the socially necessary function of retribution, the Court held. "This function may be unappealing to many, but it is essential in an ordered society that asks its citizens to rely on legal processes rather than self-help to vindicate their wrongs."

Finally, Justice Stewart was unable to say that the death penalty is a disproportionate punishment. "When a life has been taken deliberately by an offender, we cannot say that the punishment is invariably disproportionate to the crime. It is an extreme sanction, suitable to the most extreme of crimes," he concluded.

Given the carefully legislated guidelines under which Georgia administers imposition of a capital sentence, the Court found that Gregg's death sentence was constitutionally imposed.

Analyzing the Case

1. Under Georgia law, what would be one example of an aggravating circumstance?

_____

_____

_____

2. Why would the Court presume the validity of the death penalty?

_____

_____

_____

Critical Thinking

3. **Drawing Conclusions** What function does retribution by a state serve? Do you agree or disagree with such a premise?

_____

_____

_____

_____

_____

_____

_____

_____

_____

_____

_____

SUPREME COURT CASE   44

WASHINGTON V. DAVIS (1976)

Background of the Case

In 1970, African American police officers in the District of Columbia filed suit against the police commissioner and other city officials. They claimed that the police department's hiring and promotion policies were racially discriminatory. At issue was Test 21, an examination intended to test verbal ability, vocabulary, reading, and comprehension. The African American officers claimed that Test 21 was discriminatory because a higher percentage of African Americans failed the test than did whites.

A federal district court disagreed. The case went to the Court of Appeals, which ruled in the officers' favor. That decision was based solely on the fact that four times as many African Americans failed the test as did whites. The Court of Appeals held that the test was discriminatory without requiring that any additional discriminatory intent be shown or proved. City officials appealed this ruling to the United States Supreme Court.

Constitutional Issue

Several points were in question. Did the due process clause of the Fifth and Fourteenth Amendments, and the equal protection clause of the Fourteenth Amendment, prohibit racially disproportionate results? Was it necessary to prove an attempt to purposefully discriminate?

The Court's Decision

The Court ruled 7 to 2 that Test 21 did not violate the due process or equal protection clauses. Justice Byron R. White wrote for the Court.

The Court held that "the central purpose of the equal protection clause of the Fourteenth Amendment is the prevention of official conduct discriminating on the basis of race. . . . But our cases have not embraced the proposition that a law or other official act, without regard to whether it reflects a racially discriminatory purpose, is unconstitutional <u>solely</u> because it has a racially disproportionate impact."

Other Court decisions had held that the establishment of purpose was vital to determine discrimination. Even so, White stated, "a statute, otherwise neutral on its face, must not be applied so as invidiously to discriminate on the basis of race." The same was true for actions. The Court agreed it was even possible to infer discrimination "from the totality of the relevant facts, including the fact, if it is true, that the law bears more heavily on one race than another."

On the issue of Test 21, however, the Court found that African Americans no more than whites could blame failing the test on a denial of equal protection. The Court maintained that "it is untenable that the Constitution prevents the government from seeking modestly to up-grade the communicative abilities of its employees rather than to be satisfied with some lower level of competence." The Court ruled that Test 21 was "neutral on its face." Moreover, its disproportionate impact did not "warrant the conclusion that it is a purposeful device to discriminate against Negroes and hence an infringement of the constitutional rights of respondents as well as other black applicants."

Concurring, Justice Stevens wrote, "There are two reasons why I am convinced that the challenge to Test 21 is insufficient. First, the test serves the neutral and legitimate purpose of requiring all applicants to meet a uniform minimum standard of literacy. Reading ability is manifestly relevant to the police function, there is no evidence that the required passing grade was set at an arbitrarily high level, and there is sufficient disparity among high schools and high school graduates to justify the use of a separate uniform test.

Second, the same test is used throughout the federal service. . . ." Stevens wrote on this second point that he felt the objections of only the District of Columbia Police Department were not enough to change a test widely used by the federal government and accepted elsewhere in the nation.

A Dissenting Opinion

Justice William Brennan wrote a dissenting opinion. He referred to other cases in Illinois and Ohio where District Courts had reached conclusions opposite to the one the Court had reached in this case. He also expressed concern that what was being tested in Test 21 was not job-related skills, but verbal skills. He concluded that because Test 21 tests verbal ability, "Any contention that the resulting correlation between examination scores would be evidence that the initial test is 'job related' is plainly erroneous."

Analyzing the Case

1. What did the African American police officers find discriminatory about Test 21?

_____

_____

_____

2. Which element was missing according to the Supreme Court and the Appeals Court?

_____

_____

3. Under what constitutional provision was the case largely decided?

_____

_____

_____

Critical Thinking

4. **Making Comparisons** Cite one or two other examples of alleged discrimination similar to the case of Test 21.

_____

_____

_____

_____

_____

_____

_____

_____

_____

SUPREME COURT CASE   45

REGENTS OF THE UNIVERSITY OF CALIFORNIA V. BAKKE (1978)

Background of the Case

The Medical School of the University of California at Davis used a separate admissions process for minority students. In 1973 it admitted 84 regular and 16 minority or disadvantaged students—African Americans, Hispanics, Asians, or Native Americans. The latter group collectively had substantially lower science grade-point averages and median Medical College Aptitude Test scores than those in the regular-student group.

Alan Bakke, a white applicant in the same year, had a science grade-point average slightly below the median of all regular applicants, but his aptitude test scores were substantially higher. When he was refused admission, Bakke sued the Regents, the university's governing board, for a place at the medical school. California's Superior Court found that the special admissions program violated the federal and state constitutions and the 1964 Civil Rights Act. Even so, the court declined to order Bakke admitted to the school.

On appeal, the California Supreme Court supported Bakke. Citing the Fourteenth Amendment, the court ordered him admitted to the medical school. The Regents then appealed to the United States Supreme Court.

Constitutional Issue

Did the establishment of special admissions criteria for minority students violate the equal protection clause of the Fourteenth Amendment? Further, are racial-preference considerations always unconstitutional?

The Court's Decision

With two separate 5 to 4 votes and majorities, the Court ruled that the university's minority admissions program violated the equal protection clause, although a properly devised program could well be constitutional. Justice Lewis F. Powell, Jr., wrote for the Court.

Powell explained that it is "no longer possible to peg the guarantees of the Fourteenth Amendment to the struggle for equality of one racial minority. . . . Although many of the Framers of the Fourteenth Amendment conceived of its primary function as bridging the vast distance between members of the Negro race and the white 'majority,' the Amendment itself was framed in universal terms, without reference to color, ethnic origin, or condition of prior servitude." Further, the rights guaranteed by the Fourteenth Amendment do not belong to classes but to individuals. Powell stated, "The guarantee of equal protection cannot mean one thing when applied to one individual and something else when applied to a person of another color. If both are not accorded the same protection, then it is not equal."

The Court refused to adopt the view "that discrimination against members of the white 'majority' cannot be suspect if its purpose can be characterized as 'benign.'" In other words, unless it could be shown that some proven constitutional or statutory violation existed, or that the government has some compelling justification in inflicting a burden on one individual in order to help another, the Court concluded, "the preferring members of any one group for no reason other than race or ethnic origin is discrimination for its own sake. This the Constitution forbids."

The University's program failed this test because it "imposes disadvantages upon persons like respondent (Bakke), who bear no responsibility for whatever harm the beneficiaries of the special program are thought to have suffered." On the other hand, a university might well use racial criteria in an effort to insure diversity in its student body. Racial identity, however, could not be the sole criteria for admission, although it might be an important one. The Court felt that the university erred by making race the only criterion and by setting aside a fixed number of places for such applicants, thus establishing a quota system. It would still be free to devise an admissions program "involving the competitive consideration of race and ethnic origin" by making race one factor among others in the competition for all available places. Powell wrote that "a court would not assume that a university, professing to employ a nondiscriminatory admissions policy, would operate it as a cover for the functional equivalent of a quota system."

The Court concluded that "the fatal flaw in the petitioner's preferential program is its disregard of individual rights as guaranteed by the Fourteenth Amendment. Such rights are not absolute. But when a State's distribution of benefits or imposition of burdens hinges on the color of a person's skin or ancestry, that individual is entitled to a demonstration that the challenged classification is necessary to promote a substantial state interest."

Analyzing the Case

1. According to this decision, is the Fourteenth Amendment aimed at any particular minority or minorities?

_____

_____

_____

2. Why couldn't Bakke, as a white, be required to yield to disadvantaged minorities in the admissions process?

_____

_____

_____

Critical Thinking

3. **Analyzing Information** Are racial considerations always illegal?

_____

_____

_____

_____

_____

_____

_____

_____

_____

_____

_____

_____

SUPREME COURT CASE 46

KAISER ALUMINUM AND CHEMICAL CORPORATION (AND UNITED STEELWORKERS OF AMERICA) V. WEBER (1979)

Background of the Case

Title VII of the 1964 Civil Rights Act made it unlawful to discriminate in the hiring or firing of employees on the basis of race, color, religion, sex, or national origin. Likewise, it also became unlawful to "limit, segregate, or classify" employees in such a way as to deny them employment opportunities on any of those same grounds. Title VII noted, "Nothing contained in this title shall be interpreted to require any employer (or) labor organization . . . to grant preferential treatment to any individual or to any group because of . . . race, color, religion, sex, or national origin . . . on account of an imbalance which may exist with respect to the total number or percentage of persons of any race, color, religion, sex, or national origin employed by any employer. . . ." In addition, Title VII covered training, retraining, and apprenticeship programs.

In 1974 the United Steelworkers of America (USWA) and Kaiser Aluminum and Chemical Corporation signed a labor agreement applicable to 15 Kaiser plants. It included a plan to open Kaiser's nearly all-white skilled craftwork positions to African American employees.

Under this plan, instead of following its usual practice of hiring from outside, Kaiser would retrain its own workers for skilled craftwork positions. Trainees would be selected on the basis of job seniority, but 50 percent of all trainees were to be African Americans. This would continue until the percentage of African Americans among Kaiser's skilled craftworkers had risen to 39 percent, which was the percentage of blacks in the local labor force.

One effect of the plan was that African American trainees with less seniority than whites were taken into the retraining program. Brian Weber was among a group of whites rejected for retraining although he had greater seniority than any African American applicant.

Weber sued, claiming that he had been discriminated against in violation of Title VII. The Federal District Court agreed. Kaiser and the union appealed to the United States Court of Appeals, which again held in Weber's favor. An appeal was then made to the United States Supreme Court.

Constitutional Issue

Does Title VII permit a racially conscious affirmative-action plan?

The Court's Decision

The Court voted 5 to 2 against Weber. Justice William Brennan wrote for the Court.

Brennan specified the question as "the narrow statutory issue of whether Title VII *forbids* private employers and unions from voluntarily agreeing upon bona fide affirmative action plans that accord racial preferences in the manner and for the purpose provided in the Kaiser-USWA plan."

The Court held that Weber's argument was based on a literal interpretation of Title VII but that this was insufficient. Citing a previous case, Brennan said, "It is 'a familiar rule that a thing may be within the letter of the statute and yet not within the statute, because [it is] not within its spirit, nor within the intention of its makers.'"

In Brennan's opinion Congress drafted the statute in question because it "feared that the goals of the Civil Rights Act—the integration of African Americans into the mainstream of American society—could not be achieved unless this trend [discrimination based on race] was reversed." In reviewing the legislative debates, the Court was convinced that Congress had not intended to prohibit "private and voluntary affirmative action efforts as one method of solving this problem."

The Court found that "the purposes of the plan mirror those of the statute. Both were designed to break down old patterns of racial segregation and hierarchy. Both were structured to 'open employment opportunities for Negroes in occupations which have been traditionally closed to them.'"

Finally, the Court noted that nothing in the plan would result in white workers being fired to make room for African Americans, nor were whites completely unable to obtain retraining. "Moreover," Brennan said, "the plan is a temporary measure; it is not intended to maintain racial balance, but simply to eliminate a manifest racial imbalance."

A Dissenting Opinion

In Justice Burger's dissenting view, the Kaiser-USWA plan embodied the very discrimination the statute was designed to forbid. He said, "That statute was conceived and enacted to make discrimination against any individual illegal, and I fail to see how 'voluntary compliance' with the nondiscrimination principle that is the heart and soul of Title VII . . . will be achieved by permitting employers to discriminate against some individuals to give preferential treatment to others."

Analyzing the Case

1. What did the Court interpret as the true purpose of Title VII?

_____

_____

_____

2. Why did the Court think a literal reading of the statute was misleading?

_____

_____

_____

Critical Thinking

3. **Demonstrating Reasoned Judgment** Do you agree or disagree with Chief Justice Burger's dissenting opinion that the Kaiser plan was, in fact, a discriminatory one? Why?

_____

_____

_____

_____

_____

_____

_____

_____

_____

_____

SUPREME COURT CASE   47

ROSTKER V. GOLDBERG (1981)

Background of the Case

The President of the United States, by proclamation, can require the registration of every male citizen and male resident alien between the ages of 18 and 26 to facilitate conscription—enrollment for compulsory service in the armed forces. Section 3 of the Military Selective Service Act empowers the President to do this.

Registration for the draft was discontinued in 1975, but in 1980 President Carter determined that it was necessary to reactivate the registration process. He recommended that funds be transferred from the Department of Defense to the Selective Service System so this could take place.

President Carter also recommended that Congress amend the Military Selective Service Act to permit the registration and conscription of women. Congress agreed on the need to reactivate the registration process. Although Congress considered the question of extending registration and conscription to women, it decided against that action. Thus, Congress allocated only the funds necessary to register males for the draft.

Some 10 years earlier, several men subject to registration for the draft and later induction into the armed services had brought a case before the United States District Court for the Eastern District of Pennsylvania. They claimed that women as well as men should be subject to registration and conscription. A Federal District Court held that the gender-based discrimination of the Military Selective Service Act violated the due process clause of the Fifth Amendment. This case, *Rostker* v. *Goldberg,* was then heard by the United States Supreme Court.

Constitutional Issue

Does the exemption of women from registration and conscription violate the Fifth Amendment?

The Court's Decision

Chief Justice William Rehnquist wrote the opinion for the 6 to 3 majority opinion of the Court. The Court held that the exemption of women did not violate the Fifth Amendment.

The rationale for the ruling was twofold. First, Congress did not act unthinkingly in its decision to exclude women; it considered the question at great length. Also, Congress did not decide the issue on the basis of "a traditional way of thinking about women." Second, women as a group, unlike men as a group, were not eligible for combat. Thus, on this point, the Court decided that since the obvious purpose in reactivating the draft was to prepare a group of combat troops, women would not be included in that group.

At the core of this decision and accepted by Congress and the Supreme Court was the rule that women are not eligible for combat. With this as a given, the rest of the argument rested on whether or not it would still be to the country's advantage to draft women for noncombat positions instead of depending on volunteers.

The District Court had conducted research using statistics from the Defense Department that showed that some 80,000 persons would have to be conscripted to fill noncombat positions in the event of a major war. In other words, some 80,000 women could be usefully employed by the armed services in that event.

Rehnquist concluded, "In sum, Congress carefully evaluated the testimony that 80,000 women conscripts could be usefully employed in the event of a draft and rejected it in the permissible exercise of its constitutional responsibility. The District Court was quite wrong in undertaking an independent evaluation of this evidence, rather than adopting an appropriately deferential examination of Congress' evaluation of that evidence."

Rehnquist concluded his written opinion with these words: "In light of the foregoing, we conclude that Congress acted well within its constitutional authority when it authorized the registration of men, and not women, under the Military Selective Service Act. The decision of the District Court holding otherwise is accordingly reversed."

A Dissenting Opinion

Justice Thurgood Marshall wrote, in part, in his dissent, "It [the Court] upholds a statute that requires males but not females to register for the draft, and which thereby categorically excludes women from a fundamental civic obligation. Because I believe the Court's decision is inconsistent with the Constitution's guarantee of equal protection of the law, I dissent."

Analyzing the Case

1. What was the constitutional basis for the case?

_____

_____

_____

2. What were the two major points the Court made in making its decision?

_____

_____

_____

3. What was the concern of Justice Marshall?

_____

_____

_____

Critical Thinking

4. **Demonstrating Reasoned Judgment** Do you think that women should be drafted as well as men and be allowed to fill combat positions if they want to do so? Explain your answer.

_____

_____

_____

_____

_____

_____

_____

_____

_____

SUPREME COURT CASE   48

IMMIGRATION AND NATURALIZATION SERVICE V. CHADHA (1983)

Background of the Case

Jagdish Rai Chadha is an East Indian who was born in Kenya and, at the time of this case, held a British passport. He was lawfully admitted to the United States in 1966 on a nonimmigrant student visa which expired on June 30, 1972.

On October 11, 1973, the District Director of the Immigration and Naturalization Service ordered Chadha to show cause why he should not be deported for having "remained in the United States for a longer time than permitted."

A deportation hearing was held before an immigration judge on January 11, 1974. Chadha admitted that he had overstayed his visa and the hearing was adjourned to allow him to file an application for suspension of deportation.

In February 1974 Chadha's deportation was suspended on the basis of legislation that allowed such an action if the alien in question could be proved to have resided in the United States for over seven years, was of good moral character, and would suffer "extreme hardship" if deported. Chadha met these requirements.

A report of Chadha's suspension of deportation was then sent to Congress as was required by law. On December 12, 1975, Representative Eilberg, Chairman of the Judiciary Subcommittee on Immigration, Citizenship, and International Law, introduced a resolution opposing "the granting of permanent residence in the United States" to six aliens, one of whom was Chadha. This decision was based on the finding that Chadha did not meet the hardship requirement, and the resolution against him was passed without debate or recorded vote. The resolution was not submitted to the Senate or the President.

Chadha appealed the deportation order on the basis that the law allowing the House of Representatives alone to decide his fate under the legislative veto provision was unconstitutional. The Immigration and Naturalization Service agreed with Chadha. The Court of Appeals held that the House was without constitutional authority to order Chadha's deportation. It directed the Attorney General "to cease and desist from taking any steps to deport this alien based upon the resolution enacted by the House of Representatives" which it ruled to be unconstitutional as Chadha had appealed. The case was then heard by the United States Supreme Court.

Constitutional Issue

Was the one-house veto of the decision to allow Chadha to remain in the United States unconstitutional, violating the doctrine of separation of powers?

The Court's Decision

Chief Justice Warren Burger wrote the opinion for the 7 to 2 majority. In it, the Court held that, indeed, the one-house legislative veto provision of the existing law was unconstitutional because, being legislative in purpose and effect, it required passage by both houses and had to be presented to the President as well. This finding is in accordance with the procedures set out in Article I of the Constitution regarding all legislative acts.

In making the point that the one-house legislative veto was unconstitutional, Burger wrote, "The impropriety of the House's assumption of this function is confirmed by the fact that its action raises the very danger the Framers sought to avoid—the exercise of unchecked power. . . . The only effective constraint on Congress' power is political, but Congress is most accountable politically when it prescribes rules of general applicability. When it decides rights of specific persons, those rights are subject to 'the tyranny of a shifting majority.'"

A Dissenting Opinion

Justice White dissented. He expressed the view that the legislative veto is an important political invention and that neither Article I nor the doctrine of separation of powers is violated by the legislative veto.

In his dissent Justice White wrote, "Today the Court not only invalidates [a law of the] Immigration and Naturalization Act, but also sounds a death knell for nearly 200 other statutory provisions in which Congress has reserved a 'legislative veto.' For this reason, the Court's decision is of surpassing importance."

White concluded, "I regret that I am in fundamental disagreement with my colleagues on the fundamental questions that these cases represent. But even more I regret the destructive scope of the Court's holding. It reflects a profoundly different conception of the Constitution than that held by the courts which sanctioned the modern administrative state. . . . I fear it will now be more difficult to insure that the fundamental policy decisions in our society will be made not by an appointed official but by the body immediately responsible to the people. I must dissent."

Analyzing the Case

1. What was the basis of Chadha's case?

_____

_____

_____

2. Why was the one-house legislative action found unconstitutional?

_____

_____

_____

Critical Thinking

3. **Demonstrating Reasoned Judgment** Do you agree with the Court's decision? Explain your answer.

_____

_____

_____

_____

_____

_____

_____

_____

_____

_____

SUPREME COURT CASE   49

NEW JERSEY V. T.L.O. (1985)

Background of the Case

A New Jersey high school teacher discovered a 14-year-old freshman, whom the courts later referred to by her initials—T.L.O., smoking in a school lavatory. Since smoking was a violation of school rules, T.L.O. was taken to the Assistant Vice Principal's office.

When questioned by the Assistant Vice Principal, T.L.O. denied that she had been smoking. The Assistant Vice Principal then searched her purse. Upon opening the purse he found a pack of cigarettes along with rolling papers commonly used for smoking marijuana. As a result, he searched the purse more thoroughly and found marijuana, a pipe, plastic bags, a large amount of money, an index card listing students who owed T.L.O. money, and two letters that implicated T.L.O. in marijuana dealing.

The Assistant Vice Principal notified T.L.O.'s mother and turned the evidence of drug dealing over to the police. T.L.O. was charged as a juvenile with criminal activity. T.L.O., in turn, claimed the evidence of drug dealing found in her purse could not be used in Court as evidence because it was obtained through an illegal search. T.L.O.'s attorneys claimed that the Fourth Amendment protects against unreasonable search and seizure. The constitutional requirements for "probable cause" and issuing a search warrant applied to T.L.O. while in high school as a student. After appeals in the lower courts, the case eventually reached the Supreme Court.

Constitutional Issue

T.L.O.'s case raised the question of whether the Fourth Amendment required school officials to meet the same strict standards as police officers where conducting searches of students' property in school. In most instances police officers must have "probable cause" to believe that the subject of a search has violated or is violating the law, and they must obtain a proper search warrant. If these standards are not met by the police, evidence gathered from a search can be excluded from a criminal trial.

The Court's Decision

The Court ruled that (1) the Fourth Amendment ban on unreasonable searches and seizures applies to searches conducted by school officials and that (2) the search of T.L.O. was reasonable. However, the Court also ruled that school officials do not have to meet the same standards as police officers when conducting searches.

Justice Byron White wrote the Court's opinion. White noted that students have a real need to bring personal property into school and have "legitimate expectations of privacy" while in school. At the same time, White added, "against the child's interest in privacy must be set the substantial interest of teachers and administrators in maintaining discipline in the classroom and on school grounds." The Court devised a plan to ease for school officials the Fourth Amendment requirements for a lawful search. Justice White outlined two ways this could be done.

First, the Court ruled that school officials need not obtain a search warrant before searching a student who is under their supervision. "The warrant requirement," Justice White said, "is unsuited to the school environment . . . [and] would unduly interfere with the maintenance of the swift and informal disciplinary procedures needed in the schools."

Second, the Court ruled that school officials do not have to be held to the same strict "probable cause" standard that applies to police when conducting searches. In earlier cases the Court had ruled that "probable cause" meant that police must have solid information that there is a real chance the person being searched has violated or is violating the law. Instead, the Court said school officials may search a student as long as "there are reasonable grounds for suspecting that the search will turn up evidence that the student has violated or is violating either the law or the rules of the school." Thus, the Court replaced the "probable cause" requirement with a "reasonableness" requirement.

Two justices, Brennan and Marshall, disagreed strongly with letting school officials use a "reasonableness" standard instead of the same "probable cause" standard required of the police. Justice Brennan wrote, "This [idea] finds support neither in precedent nor policy and . . . [could lead to] a dangerous weakening of the purpose of the Fourth Amendment to protect the privacy and security of our citizens."

Analyzing the Case

1. Why did the Vice Principal search T.L.O.'s purse?

_____

_____

_____

2. Do you think the search was reasonable? Give reasons for your answer.

_____

_____

_____

3. What must police do to conduct a lawful search under the Fourth Amendment?

_____

_____

_____

Critical Thinking

4. **Drawing Conclusions** Why did the Supreme Court give school officials more freedom to conduct searches than the police have?

_____

_____

_____

_____

_____

_____

_____

_____

_____

_____

SUPREME COURT CASE   50

WALLACE V. JAFFREE (1985)

Background of the Case

During the 1980s, 23 states passed so-called moment-of-silence laws. These laws were designed to promote a new type of school prayer. These moment-of-silence laws varied slightly, but in general they allowed teachers to set aside a moment in each public school classroom each day for students to engage in quiet meditation. The idea was to give each student the opportunity to pray during the moment-of-silence.

Ishmael Jaffree, a parent of three school children, challenged Alabama's moment-of silence law by filing a complaint against the Mobile County, Alabama, schools. The Alabama law authorized a one-minute period of silence in all public schools "for medita-tion or voluntary prayer." Jaffree claimed the law violated the First Amendment law against the establishment of religion.

Constitutional Issue

Did a state law authorizing a daily period of silence in all public schools for the purpose of prayer violate the First Amendment?

The Court's Decision

By a 6 to 3 vote the Court ruled that the Alabama law was an endorsement of religion in the public schools and thus violated the First Amendment.

Justice John Paul Stevens wrote the majority opinion. Justice Stevens noted that the history of the Alabama law clearly indi-cated that the state "intended to change existing law and that it was motivated by the . . . purpose . . . to characterize prayer as a favored practice." Such an endorsement, Stevens argued, "is not consistent with the established principle that the government must pursue a course of complete neutrality toward religion."

Stevens explained that whenever govern-ment itself "speaks on a religious subject, one of the questions that we must ask is 'whether the government intends to convey a message of endorsement or disapproval of religion.'" The Court found that in Alabama the state legislature had passed the moment-of-silence law "to convey a message of state approval of prayer activities in the public schools."

Justices Lewis F. Powell, Jr., and Sandra Day O'Connor wrote concurring opinions which noted that some moment-of-silence laws might be constitutional. O'Connor argued that a state-sponsored moment of silence in the public schools was different from state-sponsored vocal prayer or Bible reading in two ways. First, she said, a moment-of-silence is not inherently religious. "Silence, unlike prayer or Bible reading, need not be associated with a religious exercise."

Second, pupils who take part in a moment-of-silence do not need to compro-mise their beliefs. "During a moment-of-silence," O'Connor argued, "a student who objects to prayer is left to his or her own thoughts, and is not compelled to listen to the prayers or thoughts of others." The Alabama law was unconstitutional according to O'Connor because it was very clear from the official history of the law that its "sole purpose" was "to return voluntary prayer to our public schools." In addition, O'Connor noted that the state legislature clearly wanted to use the law to encourage students to choose prayer over other alternatives during the moment-of-silence. Thus, the message actually conveyed to students and teachers was that "prayer was the endorsed activity during the state-prescribed moment-of-silence."

Dissenting Opinions

Chief Justice Warren Burger, William H. Rehnquist, and Byron White each wrote dis-senting opinions. Justice Burger captured the main dissenting idea when he stated, "It makes no sense to say that Alabama has 'endorsed prayer' by merely enacting a new statute . . . that voluntary prayer is one of the authorized activities during a moment-of-silence."

Thus, Burger argued that to suggest that a moment-of-silence law using the word *prayer* unconstitutionally endorses religion, while a similar law that avoids the word *prayer* does not endorse religion, "manifests hostility toward religion."

Burger stated, "The Alabama Legislature has no more 'endorsed' religion than a state or the Congress does when it provides for legislative chaplains, or than this Court does when it opens each session with an invocation to God."

Justice William Rehnquist reviewed the history of the First Amendment and concluded that the Framers of the Constitution intended "to prohibit the designation of any church as a 'national one.'" Nothing in the First Amendment, however, required "government to be strictly neutral between religion and irreligion." Thus, according to Rehnquist, the Constitution did not prohibit Alabama from passing a moment-of-silence law that would promote prayer "as a favored practice."

Analyzing the Case

1. What is a "moment-of-silence" law?

_____

_____

_____

2. Why was the Alabama law ruled unconstitutional?

_____

_____

_____

Critical Thinking

3. Identifying Central Issues What was the main idea of Justice Burger's dissent?

_____

_____

_____

_____

_____

_____

_____

_____

_____

_____

_____

SUPREME COURT CASE 51

BETHEL SCHOOL DISTRICT V. FRASER (1986)

Background of the Case

Matthew Fraser, a student at Bethel High School in Bethel, Washington, gave a speech to a school assembly nominating a fellow student for an elective office. About 600 high school students attended the assembly. Throughout his speech Fraser used elaborate, graphic, explicit sexual metaphors to describe his candidate.

The assembly was a regular part of a school-sponsored educational program in self-government. Students were required to attend the assembly or report to a study hall.

Fraser had discussed his speech in advance with two of his teachers. Both warned him that the speech was "inappropriate" and that he "probably should not deliver it." They added that giving the speech might have "severe consequences."

Fraser's speech disrupted the assembly. Students hooted and yelled. Others simulated the sexual activities referred to in the speech. Others appeared to be embarrassed. As a result, under the school's "disruptive-conduct rule," school officials suspended Fraser from school for two days and removed his name from a list of possible graduation speakers.

The school's rule prohibited conduct that "substantially interferes with the educational process . . . including the use of obscene, profane language or gestures." Fraser challenged the constitutionality of the school's punishment under this rule. He claimed the school's punishment violated his right to free speech as guaranteed by the First Amendment.

Constitutional Issue

The First Amendment gives adults great freedom to use whatever language they want to make what they consider a political point. Do students in high school have the same freedom? Does the First Amendment protection of free speech prevent school officials from limiting obscene or vulgar speech that could disrupt the educational process?

The Court's Decision

By a vote of 7 to 2 the Court ruled that under the First Amendment school officials have the authority to discipline students for lewd or indecent speech at school events. Chief Justice Warren Burger wrote the Court's opinion.

Burger argued that the schools have a basic responsibility to prepare students for responsible citizenship. Thus, it was appropriate for schools to prohibit the use of vulgar language in public discourse in school. Burger wrote, "The undoubted freedom to advocate unpopular and controversial views in schools and classrooms must be balanced against the society's countervailing interest in teaching students the boundaries of socially appropriate behavior."

The Court noted that the First Amendment gives wide freedom to adults in matters of political speech. Burger reasoned, however, that "simply because the use of an offensive form of expression may not be prohibited to adults making what the speaker considers a political point," it does not follow "that the same latitude must be given to children in a public school."

Indeed, Burger ruled that nothing in the Constitution stops schools from "insisting that certain modes of expression are inappropriate and subject to sanctions." Instead, Burger explained, "the determination of what manner of speech in the classroom or in school assembly is inappropriate properly rests with the schoolboard."

In the famous Supreme Court decision *Tinker* v. *Des Moines* (1969), the Supreme Court had protected the rights of students under the First Amendment to wear black armbands to school to protest the Vietnam

War. In the *Tinker* decision, the Court ruled that students do not "shed their constitutional rights to freedom of speech or expression at the schoolhouse gate." Was using obscene speech to nominate a fellow student the same as using armbands to convey a political message about the Vietnam War?

In *Tinker* the Court ruled that when school officials punished students for wearing black armbands they were censoring students' political ideas about the Vietnam War. In Fraser's case, however, the school's penalties "were unrelated to any political viewpoint." Thus, Burger concluded that the First Amendment "does not prevent the school officials from determining that to permit a vulgar and lewd speech such as . . . [Fraser's] would undermine the school's basic educational mission."

Analyzing the Case

1. For what reason did school officials punish Matthew Fraser after he gave his speech?

_____

_____

_____

2. According to the Court, how did the school's responsibility for citizenship education affect students' First Amendment rights?

_____

_____

_____

3. What principle was established in *Tinker* v. *Des Moines*?

_____

_____

_____

Critical Thinking

4. **Analyzing Information** Why didn't the *Tinker* principle apply to the Fraser case?

_____

_____

_____

_____

_____

_____

_____

_____

_____

_____

SUPREME COURT CASE 52

SOUTH DAKOTA V. DOLE (1987)

Background of the Case

The federal government provides a portion of federal highway funds to the states. A federal statute requires that a state must adopt a minimum drinking age of 21 in order to receive a portion of those federal highway funds. The law directs the Secretary of Transportation—Elizabeth Dole at the time of this case—to withhold a percentage of otherwise allocated federal funds from states "in which the purchase or public possession . . . of any alcoholic beverage by a person who is less than twenty-one years of age is lawful."

South Dakota which permitted persons 19 years old or older to purchase beer containing up to 3.2 percent of alcohol, brought a court action to challenge the constitutionality of that federal law. South Dakota claimed that the federal law described above violates the constitutional limitations on the spending power of Congress under Article I of the Constitution and that it also violates the Twenty-first Amendment.

The provisions of the Twenty-first Amendment grant that the states have what amounts to complete control over whether to permit the importation or sale of liquor and how to structure the liquor distribution system. This was the finding of the Court in *California Retail Liquor Dealers Assn.* v. *Midcal Aluminum* (1980).

South Dakota thus claimed that the setting of a state drinking age was also clearly within the "core powers" reserved to each of the states under that Amendment.

The United States District Court for the District of South Dakota dismissed the complaint and the state appealed. The case was then heard by the Court of Appeals for the Eighth District which affirmed the case brought by South Dakota. The case was then heard by the United States Supreme Court.

Constitutional Issue

Is the Twenty-first Amendment of the Constitution violated by the federal law that withholds highway funds from the states not having a minimum drinking age of 21?

The Court's Decision

Justice William Rehnquist wrote for the 7 to 2 opinion of the Court. The Court ruled that the statute of the federal government was not in violation of the Twenty-first Amendment. Although the Court ruled that Congress could not impose a national drinking age by direct legislation, it ruled that Congress could constitutionally set conditions on the receipt of federal funds. As Rehnquist wrote, "Congress has acted indirectly under its spending power to encourage uniformity in the States' drinking ages." Thus, the Court ruled that the legislation was "within constitutional bounds even if Congress may not regulate drinking ages directly." The Court held that Congress may "purchase" state compliance through attaching conditions to spending grants. The major limitation on this broad view of the spending power was that Congress could "tempt" the states with funds, but it could not "coerce" the states to comply.

In other words, the basis for the Court's ruling in this case is that there is a difference between forcing or coercing compliance (an exercise of regulatory power) and buying compliance (an exercise of spending power).

Rehnquist continued, "Our decisions have recognized that in some circumstances financial inducement offered by Congress might be so coercive as to pass the point at which pressure turns into compulsion." In this case, however, the Court relied on the fact that only 5 percent of federal highway funds were at stake and reached the conclusion that the legislation was only a "mild encouragement" to the states to change their drinking ages.

Thus, the court concluded that the law is "a valid use of the spending power."

The Court further held that the statute of legislation in question satisfies requirement for the exercise of congressional spending power to be designed "for the general welfare." Congress felt that a lack of uniformity on state drinking ages was an interstate problem that needed a solution to save lives. As Rehnquist wrote, the law in question did promote the general welfare ". . . since the means chosen by Congress to address a dangerous situation—the interstate problem resulting from the incentive, created by differing state drinking ages, for young people to combine drinking and driving—were reasonably calculated to advance the general welfare."

A Dissenting Opinion

Justice Sandra Day O'Connor dissented stating, in part, that the law in question ". . . is not a condition on spending reasonably related to the expenditure of federal funds and cannot be justified on that ground. Rather, it is an attempt to regulate the sale of liquor, an attempt that lies outside Congress' power to regulate commerce because it falls within . . . the Twenty-first Amendment."

Analyzing the Case

1. What was the constitutional basis for South Dakota's case?

_____

_____

_____

2. What was the scope of the power of Congress in this case?

_____

_____

_____

Critical Thinking

3. Demonstrating Reasoned Judgment Critics have referred to this ruling as "federal blackmail." What is your opinion of the Court's decision in this case?

_____

_____

_____

_____

_____

_____

_____

_____

_____

_____

SUPREME COURT CASE 53

HAZELWOOD SCHOOL DISTRICT V. KUHLMEIER (1988)

Background of the Case

In May of 1983 the principal of Hazelwood East High School in St. Louis County, Missouri, ordered the deletion of two pages from *Spectrum,* a student newspaper. The two pages included an article on students' experiences with pregnancy and another story discussing the impact of divorce on students at the school.

The principal objected to the story on pregnancy because he believed the girls described in the story could be easily identified even if their names were left out of the story. In addition, he said the references in the story to sexual activity were not suitable for the younger students at the school.

The principal objected to the story on divorce because it named a student who complained about her father's behavior. The principal believed the parents should have been given a chance to respond to the story.

The *Spectrum* was written and edited by the school's journalism class as part of the school curriculum. The principal also said he had "serious doubts" that the two articles fit the journalistic rules of fairness and privacy taught in the course. The three student editors of the *Spectrum* then filed a suit against the principal and school district. They claimed the principal's action violated their First Amendment rights to free speech.

In May 1985 a federal district court judge ruled against the students. In July of 1986, however, a federal appeals court overturned that ruling. The appeals court said the *Spectrum* was a public forum for student expression and was fully protected by the First Amendment. In 1987 the Supreme Court decided to hear the case.

Constitutional Issue

The principal's decision to censor the school newspaper raised a very basic constitutional question. Does the First Amendment guar-antee of freedom of speech prevent school administrators from regulating student speech in school-sponsored publications such as newspapers and yearbooks?

The Court's Decision

The Court ruled 5 to 3 against the student editors. Justice Byron White wrote the majority opinion.

White stated that the First Amendment rights of students in public schools are not exactly the same as the rights of adults in other settings. Schools, White argued, "must be able to set high standards for student speech . . . under [their] auspices—standards that may be higher than those demanded by some newspaper publishers and theatrical producers in the 'real' world—and may refuse to . . . [publish] student speech that does not meet those standards."

In the case of *Tinker* v. *Des Moines* in 1969 the Court had ruled the First Amendment gave students the right to wear black armbands to school to protest the Vietnam War. Justice White said that while the Tinker decision protected students' rights to personally express their political ideas, speech in a school-sponsored newspaper was different because it occurred "as part of the school curriculum."

A school newspaper like the *Spectrum,* the Court decided, was not "a forum for public expression" but rather a tool for teaching and learning. As a result, Justice White wrote, "educators are entitled to exercise greater control over this form of student expression to assure that participants learn whatever lessons the activity is designed to teach." Thus, White concluded, "We hold that educators do not offend the First Amendment by exercising editorial control over the style and content of student speech in school-sponsored expressive activities." School officials across the nation praised the

Court's decision. They believed it gave them more authority to regulate student conduct. One official said the decision meant that schools, "as any other publisher, have the right to decide what will and will not be published."

Dissenting Opinions

Justice William H. Brennan wrote a hard-hitting dissent. Justices Thurgood Marshall and Harry A. Blackmun joined him.

Brennan noted that the *Tinker* decision said school officials could limit student speech only if the speech threatened to "materially disrupt" schoolwork or violate the rights of others. He argued, "*Tinker* teaches us that the state educator's undeniable . . . mandate to inculcate [teach] moral and political values is not a general warrant to act as 'thought police' stifling discussion of all but state-approved topics and advocacy of all but the official position."

Brennan added that "instead of teaching children to respect the diversity of ideas that is fundamental to the American system . . . the Court today teaches youth to discount important principles of our government as mere platitudes."

Analyzing the Case

1. What articles were taken out of the *Spectrum* by the principal?

_____

_____

_____

2. What reason did the Court give for allowing school officials to censor the school paper?

_____

_____

_____

Critical Thinking

3. Demonstrated Reasoned Judgment Do you agree with the Court's decision? Give reasons for your answer.

_____

_____

_____

_____

_____

_____

_____

_____

_____

_____

_____

_____

SUPREME COURT CASE 54

SKINNER V. RAILWAY LABOR EXECUTIVES ASSOCIATION (1989)

Background of the Case

The Federal Railroad Safety Act of 1970 authorizes the Secretary of Transportation to "prescribe, as necessary, appropriate rules, regulations, orders, and standards for all areas of railroad safety."

In the past, studies have shown that the problem of alcohol use by railroad employees was substantial. One study conducted by the Federal Railroad Administration (FRA) in 1979 concluded that "an estimated one out of every eight railroad workers drank at least once while on duty during the study year. In addition, 5% of workers reported to work 'very drunk' or got 'very drunk' on duty at least once in the study year. . . ."

For many years, railroads have prohibited operating employees from possession of alcohol and from consuming alcohol while on duty or on call for duty. This prohibition has been extended to include the use of other drugs as well. An employee found in violation of this rule is dismissed from his or her job.

As strict as the rules had been, the FRA recognized that alcohol and drug use by railroad employees continued to occur. After a review of accident investigations, the FRA found that between 1972 and 1983 there were a minimum of 21 significant train accidents, involving 25 fatalities, with alcohol or drug use as probable cause.

In 1985, in an attempt to curb these accidents, the FRA issued new regulations that required mandatory blood and urine testing of all railroad crew members involved in major train accidents. Any accident involving a fatality, the release of hazardous material including an evacuation and/or reported injury, or damages to railroad property of $50,000 or more would mandate the new testing.

Railway labor organizations filed suit against these FRA regulations claiming that employee rights under the Fourth Amendment would be violated. The initial trial ruled in favor of the FRA, but the Court of Appeals reversed that decision and the case was then heard by the United States Supreme Court.

Constitutional Issue

Does the FRA regulation requiring mandatory blood and urine testing after a major accident violate employees rights under the Fourth Amendment?

The Court's Decision

Justice Anthony M. Kennedy delivered the opinion of the Court which held that (1) the Fourth Amendment was applicable to drug and alcohol testing mandated or authorized by FRA regulations, but (2) drug and alcohol tests mandated or authorized by the regulations were reasonable under the Fourth Amendment even though there was no requirement of a warrant or a reasonable suspicion that any particular employee might be impaired. This conclusion was justified because the compelling government interest served by the regulations outweighed employees' privacy concerns.

Justice Kennedy wrote, "In light of . . . the surpassing safety interests served by toxicological tests in this context . . . we hold that the alcohol and drug tests contemplated by . . . the FRA's regulations are reasonable within the meaning of the Fourth Amendment. The judgment of the Court of Appeals is accordingly reversed."

Dissenting Opinions

Justice Thurgood Marshall offered his dissenting opinion as he wrote: "In permitting the Government to force entire crews to submit to invasive blood and urine tests, even when it lacks any evidence of drug or alcohol use or other wrongdoing, the majority today joins those shortsighted courts which have already allowed basic constitutional rights to fall prey to momentary emergencies."

Marshall particularly objected that the Court decision seemed to ignore the "probable cause" requirement for search and seizure under the Fourth Amendment. He spoke out against any exception, in this case defending the rights of all railroad employees who showed no evidence of drug or alcohol abuse and would be forced to be tested anyway.

The issue of invasion of privacy and the intrusive nature of the blood and urine tests also concerned Marshall. He wrote, "I find nothing minimal about the intrusion on individual liberty whenever the Government forcibly draws and analyzes a person's blood and urine." Marshall felt that some corroborating evidence such as the observance by a co-worker of impaired behavior should be required before testing. He also felt that only those workers should be tested who could reasonably be suspected of impaired behavior and whose specific actions could have caused the accident. He concluded, "Ultimately, today's decision will reduce the privacy all citizens may enjoy. . . . I dissent."

Analyzing the Case

1. Why did the Court rule that the proposed FRA testing program was more important than employees' privacy?

_____

_____

_____

2. Explain why Justice Marshall felt so strongly that the Court's decision was "shortsighted" and wrong.

_____

_____

_____

Critical Thinking

3. **Demonstrating Reasoned Judgment** Do you agree with the Court's decision? Why or why not?

_____

_____

_____

_____

_____

_____

_____

_____

_____

_____

SUPREME COURT CASE 55

CRUZAN V. DIRECTOR, MISSOURI DEPARTMENT OF HEALTH (1990)

Background of the Case

Nancy Cruzan was involved in an automobile accident and sustained serious injuries resulting in permanent brain damage. She was in what is medically termed a "persistent vegetative state" in a Missouri state hospital with the state paying for her care. In other words, there are no brain functions operational in the patient, and there is no medical diagnosis that indicates the patient will ever recover.

Cruzan's parents requested that Nancy be allowed to die which would involve taking her off the artificial nutrition and hydration systems in the hospital. Hospital employees refused to do this, knowing that her death would result.

The case was heard in a state trial which authorized taking her off the systems. The court said that a person in Nancy Cruzan's condition has a fundamental right under the State and Federal Constitutions to make the choice about death-prolonging procedures. The lower court based this ruling on the fact that Nancy had told a former housemate that she would not want to be kept alive by artificial means if she were injured to the point that she could not live "at least halfway normally."

The State Supreme Court reversed the lower court's decision. That court decided that the state's "living will" statute expressed a state policy strongly favoring the preservation of life. Nancy's parents did not have the right to terminate her medical treatment, the court ruled, unless an official living will document existed which Nancy had signed to indicate her wishes should she become incompetent to make her own decisions. The court also ruled that Cruzan's statements to her housemate were unreliable for the purpose of determining Nancy's intent. The case was then heard by the United States Supreme Court.

Constitutional Issue

Does the Constitution protect the liberty of seriously ill patients to be free from life-sustaining medical treatment? Did Nancy Cruzan's parents have the right to act in her behalf and end life-sustaining medical treatment?

The Court's Decision

The Court ruled 5 to 4 upholding the ruling of the State Supreme Court that the judgment of family members in this situation was not sufficient to end life-sustaining treatment.

Chief Justice William Rehnquist wrote for the Court. In summary, the Court held that (1) the United States Constitution did not forbid Missouri from requiring clear and convincing evidence of an incompetent's wishes to the withdrawal of life-sustaining treatment, (2) the State Supreme Court was constitutionally within its rights when it declared that trial evidence was not "clear and convincing evidence" that Cruzan would herself request her treatment to stop, and (3) due process did not require the state to accept the judgment of a family member on this matter without substantial proof that their views were those of the patient. On this last point, if a living will document had been completed by Nancy to the effect that she would allow her parents to carry out her wish to be taken off life-supporting systems, this document would have served as "substantial proof."

Sympathizing with Nancy's parents while defending the Court's decision, Rehnquist wrote, "No doubt is engendered by anything in this record but that Nancy Cruzan's mother and father are loving and caring parents. If the State were required to repose a right of 'substituted judgment' with anyone, the Cruzans would surely qualify. But we do not think the due process clause requires the

State to repose judgment on these matters with anyone but the patient herself. . . ."

A Dissenting Opinion

Justice William Brennan wrote one of the dissenting opinions. He, along with the other justices who dissented, did not find that there was any constitutional mandate that would decide this case.

Brennan wrote, "The State has no legitimate general interest in someone's life, completely abstracted from the interest of that person living that life, that could outweigh the person's choice to avoid medical treatment." He concluded, "Because I believe that Nancy Cruzan has a fundamental right to be free of unwanted . . . [medical treatment] . . . , which right is not outweighed by any interests of the State, and because I find that the improperly biased procedural obstacles imposed by the Missouri Supreme Court impermissibly burden that right, I respectfully dissent. Nancy Cruzan is entitled to die with dignity."

Analyzing the Case

1. On what factors did the State Supreme Court base its decision not to allow the Cruzans to withdraw treatment?

_____

_____

_____

2. What would constitute "clear and convincing evidence" that Nancy Cruzan wanted to end her treatment and thus her life?

_____

_____

_____

Critical Thinking

3. **Demonstrating Reasoned Judgment** What is your opinion of living wills? Do you think they are a good idea?

_____

_____

_____

_____

_____

_____

_____

_____

_____

_____

SUPREME COURT CASE 56

MICHIGAN DEPARTMENT OF STATE POLICE V. SITZ (1990)

Background of the Case

The Michigan State Police established a highway sobriety checkpoint program in early 1986 in an attempt to curb drunken driving. They created guidelines about sites selected, checkpoint operations, and publicity. According to the guidelines, all vehicles passing through a checkpoint would be stopped and their drivers would be briefly examined for signs of intoxication. If a checkpoint officer detected signs of intoxication, the motorist would be pulled over out of the flow of traffic where his or her license and registration would be examined. If further sobriety tests were warranted, these would be conducted. If the driver was found to be intoxicated, he or she would be arrested.

The first and only sobriety checkpoint conducted before this case was decided occurred in Saginaw County. During the 1 hour and 15 minutes of the check period, 126 vehicles were checked. Two drivers were detained for further tests; one of them was subsequently arrested. Another driver who drove through the checkpoint without stopping was also arrested for driving under the influence. The average delay for each vehicle was 25 seconds.

The day before that checkpoint operation, a group of licensed Michigan drivers filed suit in a county courthouse to oppose the operation of sobriety checkpoints. After a trial, the court ruled that the state's program violated the Fourth Amendment.

The State Court of Appeals agreed, stating in part that checkpoint programs are generally ineffective in curbing drunken driving. The Court of Appeals also ruled that although the objective intrusion on individual rights during a checkpoint operation is minor, the subjective intrusion is substantial. (The fear and surprise felt by law-abiding motorists at the checkpoints were described as subjective intrusion.) The case was then heard by the Supreme Court of the United States.

Constitutional Issue

Does "seizure," as defined by the Fourth Amendment, occur during a sobriety checkpoint? If so, is it "reasonable"? Does the entire checkpoint sobriety program violate the Fourth and Fourteenth Amendments?

The Court's Decision

Justice William H. Rehnquist delivered the opinion of the Court which ruled against the Michigan motorists. He concluded that highway sobriety checkpoints do not violate the Fourth and Fourteenth Amendments. Therefore, the Court reversed the decision of the Court of Appeals of Michigan.

Rehnquist referred to previous Court decisions related to police stopping motorists on public highways. In *United States* v. *Martinez-Fuerte*, highway checkpoint stops for detecting illegal aliens were ruled to be constitutional.

Fourth Amendment seizure occurs "when there is a governmental termination of freedom of movement through means intentionally applied." Rehnquist agreed with the lower courts that "seizure" as defined by the Fourth Amendment does take place when a vehicle is stopped at a checkpoint. However, he disagreed that the seizure was unreasonable.

In deciding the "reasonableness" of the checkpoint operation Rehnquist weighed the relative need to reduce drunken driving against the measure of intrusion on motorists. He wrote: "No one can seriously dispute the magnitude of the drunken driving problem or the States' interest in eradicating it." He quoted current statistics concerning the tremendous toll caused by drunken driving. At that time, the statistics revealed that in the span of one year over 25,000 deaths, one million personal injuries, and more than five billion dollars in property damage were caused by intoxicated drivers. Rehnquist continued, "Conversely, the weight bearing on the other scale—the measure of intrusion on motorists stopped at sobriety checkpoints—is slight."

A Dissenting Opinion

Justice John Paul Stevens disagreed with the Court that the seizure involved in this case was warranted and reasonable. He referred to sobriety checkpoints as "elaborate, and disquieting, publicity stunts." He also felt that the subjective intrusion on motorists was substantial since most sobriety checkpoints occur at night and count on the element of surprise. Roving patrols that occur at night had been ruled to create substantial subjective intrusion in previous cases decided by the Court.

Stevens wrote, "This is a case that is driven by nothing more than symbolic state action—an insufficient justification for an otherwise unreasonable program of random seizures. Unfortunately, the Court is transfixed by the wrong symbol—the illusory prospect of punishing countless intoxicated motorists—when it should keep its eyes on the road plainly marked by the Constitution."

Analyzing the Case

1. What is Justice Rehnquist's view regarding the reasonableness of Fourth Amendment seizure in this case?

_____

_____

_____

2. Explain the difference in opinion between Justices Rehnquist and Stevens on the issue of subjective intrusion.

_____

_____

_____

Critical Thinking

3. **Demonstrating Reasoned Judgment** Do you think that Fourth Amendment rights have been violated by this decision? Explain your answer.

_____

_____

_____

_____

_____

_____

_____

_____

SUPREME COURT CASE 57

BOARD OF EDUCATION OF OKLAHOMA PUBLIC SCHOOLS V. DOWELL (1991)

Background of the Case

In 1961, several African American students and their parents sued the Board of Education of Oklahoma City in an attempt to end alleged segregation of the city's public schools. In 1972, the District Court for the Western District of Oklahoma ruled that previous efforts had not been successful in eliminating school segregation. They found that the city had intentionally segregated both schools and housing in the past in violation of the Fourteenth Amendment. They therefore ordered the adoption of a desegregation plan. A federal court order called for (1) mandatory student assignments for many specified schools and grades and (2) school busing.

Then, in 1977, the District Court sought to end the desegregation order claiming that the desegregation plan had been successful and a "unitary" school system had been achieved. The federal court order was lifted at that time, but the desegregation decree was not dissolved.

Later, the Oklahoma City School Board did again adopt a student reassignment plan to begin in the 1985–1986 school year. This plan contained busing and also some school assignment by neighborhood. It also allowed a student's voluntary transfer from a school in which the student was in the majority to a school in which the student was a minority. African American students and their parents protested that these actions were insufficient and that the school district had not achieved the "unitary" status that they claimed they had accomplished.

The schools had become more segregated along neighborhood lines, so students and their parents filed a petition to reopen the lawsuit. The District Court refused, saying that segregation was the result of local economics, and that it was not a lingering effect of former intentional school segregation.

The case then went to the 10th Circuit Court of Appeals which reversed the District Court decision and said that the Western District of Oklahoma's desegregation decree of 1972 should remain in effect and a stricter standard should be used to measure school policies. The case was then heard by the United States Supreme Court.

Constitutional Issue

Was the Oklahoma City School District operating in compliance with the commands of the equal protection clause of the Fourteenth Amendment?

The Court's Decision

Justice William H. Rehnquist wrote for the 5 to 3 majority decision of the Supreme Court. The Court ruled that the Board of Education of the Oklahoma City Public Schools was acting in compliance with the equal protection clause of the Fourteenth Amendment and that the former federal decree did not have to be reactivated. In the Court's opinion, formerly segregated school districts may be freed of school busing orders if they can prove that any elements of past discrimination have been removed to all "practicable" extent. The case was then remanded, or sent back, to the District Court for further proceedings.

In delivering the opinion of the Court, Rehnquist wrote: "The Court of Appeals' test for dissolving a desegregation decree is more stringent than is required by this Court's decisions dealing with the injunctions or by the Equal Protection Clause of the Fourteenth Amendment."

Rehnquist wrote that federal supervision of local school systems has always been meant to be a temporary measure. Only if a violation of the Constitution occurs should federal authority be returned. In this case, there is no such violation. He went on to say that the school district had acted in good-faith compliance by busing students for more than a decade. Private decision making and economics, he wrote, were more the causes of segregation than were school district policies.

A Dissenting Opinion

Now-retired Justice Thurgood Marshall wrote a dissent. He wrote, in part, "In order to assess the full consequences of lifting the decree at issue in this case, it is necessary to explore more fully than does the majority the history of racial segregation in the Oklahoma City schools. This history reveals nearly unflagging resistance by the Board to judicial efforts to dismantle the City's dual education system."

Marshall felt that the purposes of the former federal decree had not been reached and that further steps should be taken to avoid one-race schools. He wrote: "Because the record here shows, and the Court of Appeals found, that feasible steps could be taken to avoid one-race schools, it is clear that the purposes of the decree have not yet been achieved and the Court of Appeals' reinstatement of the decree should be affirmed. I therefore dissent."

Analyzing the Case

1. What were the two main parts of the federal court order for desegregation?

_____

_____

_____

2. What was the constitutional basis for the suit brought by the African American parents and students?

_____

_____

_____

Critical Thinking

3. **Identifying Central Issues** What were the concerns of Justice Marshall as expressed in his dissenting opinion?

_____

_____

_____

_____

_____

_____

_____

_____

_____

SUPREME COURT CASE 58

CALIFORNIA V. ACEVEDO (1991)

Background of the Case

On October 28, 1987, Officer Coleman of the Santa Ana, California, Police Department received a call from a federal drug enforcement agent in Hawaii. The agent told Coleman that he had seized a Federal Express package containing marijuana that had been addressed to a man named Acevedo living in Santa Ana. The agent sent the package to Coleman instead, instructing him to take it to the Federal Express office and arrest the person who came to claim it.

On October 30, Coleman observed as a man arrived to claim the package. Police officers continued to observe as he drove to his apartment and took the package inside. A brief time later, a different man left the apartment carrying a knapsack that appeared to be half full. Police officers stopped the man as he was driving off, searched the knapsack, and found 1 1/2 pounds of marijuana. About an hour later, Acevedo arrived and went into the apartment. He reappeared carrying a full brown paper bag which he deposited in the trunk of his car. Police officers stopped Acevedo, opened the trunk and the bag, and found the marijuana.

Acevedo was charged in state court with possession of marijuana for sale. He moved that the marijuana found in his car trunk should be suppressed, that is, not allowed as admissible evidence against him. The motion was denied. He then plead guilty but appealed the denial of the suppression motion. The case then went to the California Court of Appeals which ruled in Acevedo's favor that the marijuana found in the bag in his trunk should have been suppressed. This ruling was based on an earlier case—*United States* v. *Chadwick* (1977).

According to the ruling in that case, if there is probable cause to search only a container in a car, and not the entire car itself, police need a warrant for that purpose. Thus police officers could have seized the bag and held it, but could not open it without first obtaining a warrant to do so. In *United States* v. *Ross* (1982), however, it was ruled that if there is probable cause to search a car, then the entire car, including any closed container in it, can be searched without a warrant.

The Supreme Court of California denied the petition for review, and the case then went to the United States Supreme Court.

Constitutional Issue

The Fourth Amendment protects the "right of the people to be secure in their persons, houses, papers, and effects, against unreasonable searches and seizures." Is a police search of a suspect container in a car without a warrant in violation of those Fourth Amendment rights?

The Court's Decision

Justice Harry A. Blackmun delivered the opinion of the Court. This decision was that police may search a container in an automobile without a warrant as long as there is probable cause to search that container. There does not have to be probable cause to search the entire automobile.

Blackmun wrote for the Court, "The line between probable cause to search a vehicle and probable cause to search a package in that vehicle is not always clear. . . . " Here he referred to the confusion created between the rulings in *Chadwick* and *Ross*.

Scalia wrote, "The Fourth Amendment does not by its terms require a prior warrant for searches and seizures; it merely prohibits searches and seizures that are 'unreasonable.' . . . In my view, the path out of this confusion should be sought by returning to the principle that the 'reasonableness' requirement of the Fourth Amendment affords the protection that the common law afforded."

A Dissenting Opinion

Justice John Paul Stevens argued for the stricter interpretation of the Fourth Amendment and the need for a warrant in circumstances such as found in the *Acevedo* case. He wrote: "Our decisions have always acknowledged that the warrant requirement imposes a burden on law enforcement. And our cases have not questioned that trained professionals normally make reliable assessments of the existence of probable cause to conduct a search. We have repeatedly held, however, that these factors are outweighed by the individual interest in privacy. . . . The Fourth Amendment dictates that the privacy interest is paramount, no matter how marginal the risk of error might be if the legality of warrantless searches were judged only after the fact."

Stevens continued to express grave concern about the Court's decision: "It is too early to know how much freedom America has lost today. The magnitude of the loss is, however, not nearly as significant as the Court's willingness to inflict it without even a colorable [reasonable] basis for its rejection of prior law. I respectfully dissent."

Analyzing the Case

1. What was the constitutional basis of this case?

_____

_____

_____

2. Explain the difference in the position of Justice Blackmun and the position of Justice Stevens.

_____

_____

_____

Critical Thinking

3. **Demonstrating Reasoned Judgment** Do you think your right to privacy has been compromised by this ruling? Explain your answer.

_____

_____

_____

_____

_____

_____

_____

_____

_____

SUPREME COURT CASE 59

INTERNATIONAL UNION, UAW V. JOHNSON CONTROLS, INC. (1991)

Background of the Case

Johnson Controls, Inc. manufactures batteries. The element lead is an ingredient used during the manufacturing process. Exposure to lead involves health risks, including the risk of harm to any fetus carried by a female employee. Before the Civil Rights Act of 1964, Johnson Controls did not employ any woman in a battery-manufacture job. In 1977, the company announced a warning policy that stated that a woman expecting a child should not choose a job in which she would be exposed to lead. This policy stated that there was evidence that women exposed to lead had a higher rate of abortion and that it was, "medically speaking, just good sense not to run that risk if you want children and do not want to expose the unborn child to risk, however small. . . ." The company also required that a woman sign a statement that she had been advised of the risks to her unborn child while she was exposed to lead.

Then in 1982 the company instituted a policy excluding all female employees medically capable of bearing children from lead-exposing jobs. Beginning in 1982, these women were barred from any job that involved actual or potential lead exposure exceeding Occupational Safety and Health Administration (OSHA) standards. Female employees who had medical proof that they could not bear children were the only women allowed to hold lead-exposing jobs.

A group of employees filed a class action suit against the company, claiming that the company policy constituted sex discrimination in violation of the Civil Rights Act of 1964. Among those employees were Mary Craig, who had chosen to be sterilized in order to keep her job, and Elsie Nason, a 50-year-old divorcee who had suffered a loss in pay when she was transferred out of a lead-exposing job. Both the United States District Court for the Eastern District of Wisconsin and the Court of Appeals ruled in favor of the employer. The case was then heard by the United States Supreme Court.

Constitutional Issue

Was the company policy discriminatory and in violation of employees civil rights as put forth in the Civil Rights Act of 1964? May an employer lawfully exclude a fertile female employee from certain jobs because of its concern for the health of the children she might bear?

The Court's Decision

The Court decided 6 to 3 in favor of the employees. Justice Harry A. Blackmun delivered the opinion of the Court which held that an employer could not exclude a female employee from certain jobs because of concern for the health of a fetus she might conceive.

Justice Blackmun wrote, "The bias in Johnson Controls' policy is obvious. Fertile men, but not fertile women, are given the choice as to whether they wish to risk their reproductive health for a particular job." Further, he wrote that the company policy was in violation of the Civil Rights Act of 1964 which "prohibits sex-based classifications in terms of conditions of employment, in hiring and discharging decisions, and in other employment decisions that adversely affect an employee's status." Title VII of that Act further "mandates that decisions about welfare of future children be left to the parents who conceive, bear, support, and raise them rather than to the employers who hire those parents or the courts."

Justice Blackmun also cited the Pregnancy Discrimination Act of 1978. "The Pregnancy Discrimination Act has now made clear that . . . discrimination based on a woman's pregnancy is, on the face of it, discrimination because of her sex." Further, "It is no more appropriate for the courts than it is for individual employers to decide whether a woman's reproductive role is more important to her and her family than is her economic role. Congress has left this choice to the woman as hers to make."

In regard to the safety issue, Blackmun wrote, "Our case law, therefore, makes clear that the safety exception is limited to instances in which sex or pregnancy actually interferes with the employees ability to perform the job." Further, "Fertile women, as far as appears in the record, participate in the manufacture of batteries as efficiently as anyone else."

Justice White, while concurring in the decision of the Court, wrote that "a fetal protection policy would be justified [under law] . . . if an employer could show that exclusion of women from certain jobs was reasonably necessary to avoid substantial tort liability." He took the position that many employers are now being sued for damages by children who suffered prenatal injuries and that companies should be able to protect themselves to some extent. He agreed, however, that the policy of Johnson Controls was unacceptable.

Justice Scalia also had some reservations, although concurring with the Court's decision. He wrote, "I think, for example, that a shipping company may refuse to hire pregnant women as crew members on long voyages because the on-board facilities for foreseeable emergencies, though quite feasible, would be inordinately expensive."

Analyzing the Case

1. Why did Johnson Controls seek to exclude women from lead-exposing jobs?

_____

_____

_____

2. How did the company's policy violate the Civil Rights Act of 1964?

_____

_____

_____

Critical Thinking

3. Evaluating Information What concern did Justice White voice? Do you agree or disagree?

_____

_____

_____

_____

_____

_____

_____

_____

_____

_____

SUPREME COURT CASE 60

ARIZONA V. FULMINANTE (1991)

Background of the Case

After Oreste Fulminante's 11-year-old step-daughter Jeneane was murdered in Arizona, he left Arizona and was later convicted of an unrelated federal crime and imprisoned in New York. Anthony Sarivola, a fellow inmate and paid informant for the FBI, befriended Fulminante.

Sarivola knew that Fulminante was the target of tough treatment from other inmates who had heard that he was a possible child murderer. He offered Fulminante protection from other inmates if he would tell him the truth. Fulminante agreed and told Sarivola that he had, indeed, killed his stepdaughter. He provided convincing details of the crime which he also confessed to Sarivola's wife once he was released from prison.

On the basis of these confessions, Fulminante was indicted in Arizona for first-degree murder. Fulminante protested that there had been a violation of his rights to due process under the Fifth and Fourteenth Amendments; he claimed that his confessions had been "coerced" and therefore should not be admissible as evidence against him. A 1967 ruling had said that a coerced confession can never be considered "harmless error" and was always grounds for overturning a conviction.

The trial court, however, denied Fulminante's motion to suppress the confessions and found that both confessions had been voluntary. The state introduced both confessions as evidence at trial and Fulminante was convicted of murder and sentenced to death. The Arizona Supreme Court, however, reversed Fulminante's conviction and ruled that he be retried without the use of the first confession which that court judged to be coerced. The case was then heard by the Supreme Court of the United States.

Constitutional Issue

Was the accused deprived of his constitutional rights to due process as described in the Fifth and Fourteenth Amendments? Were his confessions coerced and, therefore, inadmissible as evidence?

The Court's Decision

Justice Byron R. White delivered the opinion of the Court affirming the judgment of the Arizona Supreme Court. He concluded "The Arizona Supreme Court ruled in this case that respondent Oreste Fulminante's confession, received in evidence at his trial for murder, had been coerced and that its use against him was barred by the Fifth and Fourteenth Amendments to the United States Constitution. The court also ruled that the harmless-error rule could not be used to save the conviction. We affirm the judgment of the Arizona court, although for different reasons than those on which that court relied."

Further explaining the Court's finding, Justice White continued by stating that as the State Supreme Court found "there was a credible threat of physical violence sufficient to support a finding of coercion." White made the point that without the confessions, which relied on one another for their effect on the jury, Fulminante likely could not have been convicted. He noted that the physical evidence at the scene of the crime and other circumstantial evidence would not have been enough to convict Fulminante. He wrote, "The transcript discloses that both the trial court and the State recognized that a successful prosecution depended on the jury believing the two confessions." He concluded: "Because a majority of the Court has determined that Fulminante's confession to Anthony Sarivola was coerced and because a majority has determined that admitting this confession was not harmless beyond a reasonable doubt, we agree with the Arizona Supreme Court's ruling that Fulminante is entitled to a new trial at which the confession is not admitted. Accordingly the judgment of the Arizona Supreme Court is affirmed."

Justice Kennedy wrote, concurring with the judgment, "In the interests of providing a clear mandate to the Arizona Supreme Court in this capital case, I deem it proper to accept in the case before us the holding of the five justices that the confession was coerced and inadmissible. I agree with a majority of the Court that admission of the confession could not be harmless error when viewed in light of all the other evidence; and so I concur in the judgment to affirm the ruling of the Arizona Supreme Court."

The key point in this case, in spite of the fact that Fulminante did receive a new trial, is that a majority of the justices agreed that a coerced confession is subject to harmless-error analysis. This reverses the 1967 ruling described above. Now a new precedent has been set: A coerced confession, introduced at trial, does not necessarily reverse a conviction.

Analyzing the Case

1. What was the ruling of the original trial court? of the Arizona Supreme Court?

_____

_____

_____

2. What was the constitutional basis for Fulminante's case?

_____

_____

_____

3. How did this case change the 1967 ruling about coerced confessions?

_____

_____

_____

Critical Thinking

4. **Demonstrating Reasoned Judgment** Do you agree with the ruling of the Court? Why or why not?

_____

_____

_____

_____

_____

_____

_____

_____

SUPREME COURT CASE   61

COUNTY OF RIVERSIDE V. MCLAUGHLIN (1991)

Background of the Case

Donald Lee McLaughlin was arrested without a warrant and brought to the Riverside County Jail in Riverside County, California. More than 36 hours passed before a probable determination took place. (A probable cause hearing consists of a judge deciding whether the arrest was justified.) McLaughlin brought a class action suit on behalf of himself and "all others similarly situated," claiming that Fourth Amendment rights had been violated. He based his suit on the ruling in *Gerstein* v. *Pugh* (1983). This case had devised a promptness requirement stating that persons arrested without a warrant must be provided probable cause determinations within 36 hours because that was sufficient time "to complete the administrative steps incident to arrest." This meant that *Gerstein* had determined that 36 hours was enough time for all of the paperwork and other procedures that have to be done before either a probable cause hearing, a bail hearing, or an arraignment hearing.

Riverside County's standard procedure was to combine its probable cause determinations with its arraignment proceedings. County policy under the California Penal Code was that arraignments must be conducted without unnecessary delay and within two days—48 hours—of the arrest. Because the probable cause determinations were held along with the arraignments, the period of waiting was more than 36 hours. Further, the two-day requirement excluded weekends and holidays, so a person arrested without a warrant late in the week could be held as long as five days before receiving probable cause determination. Over the Thanksgiving holiday, in fact, a seven-day delay is possible.

In March 1989, McLaughlin and other plaintiffs asked the District Court to issue a preliminary injunction requiring the county to provide all persons arrested without a warrant with a judicial determination of probable cause within 36 hours of arrest. The District Court did issue the injunction, holding that the county's existing practice violated the Supreme Court's decision in *Gerstein*.

The United States Court of Appeals for the Ninth Circuit combined this case with an identical injunction against the County of San Bernardino, California. It appeared that McLaughlin and the other petitioners had won their case.

The Second Circuit, however, held a different interpretation of the finding in Gerstein and said that that case had called for "the need for flexibility" and that Gerstein had also ruled to permit states to combine probable cause determinations with other pretrial proceedings.

At this point, the United States Supreme Court agreed to hear the case to resolve the conflict among the circuit courts as to what constitutes a "prompt" probable cause determination.

Constitutional Issue

The Fourth Amendment requires that persons arrested without a warrant must be brought promptly before a judge for a judicial determination of probable cause. Were McLaughlin's constitutional rights under the Fourth Amendment violated because he waited more than 36 hours for such a proceeding?

The Court's Decision

Justice Sandra Day O'Connor delivered the 5 to 4 opinion of the Court. The Supreme Court ruled that the Fourth Amendment does not compel immediate determination of probable cause upon completion of the administrative steps to warrantless arrest. Further, the Court ruled that the states were within their rights to set up combination hearings like those in Riverside County.

Lastly, a new 48-hour period was established as permissible between the time of a warrantless arrest and a probable cause proceeding.

The Court ruled, however, that even if the 48-hour standard is met, a person arrested can establish Fourth Amendment violation if he or she can prove that there was an unreasonable delay. Examples of unreasonable delay include delay for gathering additional evidence to justify arrest, delay motivated by ill will against the person arrested, and delay for delay's sake.

O'Connor stated for the Court that if the 48-hour standard is not met, the burden of proof "shifts to the government to demonstrate the existence of a bona fide [real] emergency or other extraordinary circumstance. The fact that in a particular case it may take longer than 48 hours to consolidate pretrial proceedings does not qualify as an extraordinary circumstance. Nor, for that matter, do intervening weekends. . . ."

Concerning Riverside County specifically, O'Connor stated, "The record indicates, however, that the County's current policy and practice do not comport [comply] fully with the principles we have outlined." She wrote, "The County's regular practice exceeds the 48-hour period we deem constitutionally permissible. . . ."

Analyzing the Case

1. Explain the constitutional basis for McLaughlin's case.

_____

_____

_____

2. What would constitute "unreasonable delay" even if the 48-hour standard were met?

_____

_____

_____

Critical Thinking

3. **Demonstrating Reasoned Judgment** Do you think that this ruling more strongly supports the rights of the states or the rights of the person arrested without a warrant? Explain your answer.

_____

_____

_____

_____

_____

_____

_____

_____

_____

_____

SUPREME COURT CASE   62

RUST V. SULLIVAN (1991)

Background of the Case

Regulations have been set by the Department of Health and Human Services under Title X of the Public Health Service Act of 1970. These regulations do not allow federally funded family planning clinics to provide abortion counseling, referral, or advocacy. Originally, the law had stated that no federal funds could be used in "programs where abortion is a method of family planning." During the Reagan administration, however, there was a clear and purposeful attempt to extend the law to also ban any abortion counseling at these clinics.

Planned Parenthood and the city of New York sued, saying that the law only meant that no money would be provided for abortions. They also held that the regulations infringed on the doctors' First Amendment rights and interfered with a woman's privacy right to abortion and her ability to hear competent medical advice.

The United States District Court for the Southern District of New York upheld the regulations and the plaintiffs appealed. The Court of Appeals for the Second Circuit affirmed the decision of the district court, so the plaintiffs sought to have the Supreme Court hear the case which the Court agreed to do.

Constitutional Issues

Do the regulations banning abortion counseling at federally funded clinics violate the First Amendment free speech rights of the staff and patients? Do these regulations violate a woman's Fifth Amendment right to choose whether to terminate a pregnancy?

The Court's Decision

Chief Justice William Rehnquist wrote for the 5 to 4 opinion of the Court. The Court held that (1) the regulations were allowable under the law prohibiting use of Title X

funds in programs in which abortion is a method of family planning; (2) the regulations do not violate First Amendment free speech rights of Title X fund recipients, their staffs, or their patients; and (3) the regulations do not violate a woman's Fifth Amendment right to choose to terminate a pregnancy or infringe on the doctor-patient relationship.

Rehnquist wrote, "There is no question but that the statutory prohibition contained in . . . [the law] . . . is constitutional. In *Maher* v. *Roe, supra,* we upheld a state welfare regulation under which Medicaid recipients received payments for services related to childbirth, but not for therapeutic abortions. The Court rejected a claim that this unequal subsidization [funding] worked a violation of the Constitution. We held that the government may "make a value judgment favoring childbirth over abortion, and . . . implement that judgment by the allocation of public funds." He continued, "The Government can, without violating the Constitution, selectively fund a program to encourage certain activities it believes to be in the public interest, without at the same time funding an alternative program which seeks to deal with the problem in another way. In so doing, the Government has not discriminated on the basis of viewpoint; it has merely chosen to fund one activity to the exclusion of the other."

Regarding the question of infringing on First Amendment rights, the Court stated, "Individuals who are voluntarily employed in the Title X project must perform their duties in accordance with the regulations on abortion counseling and referrals. The employees remain free, however, to pursue abortion-related activities when they are not acting under the auspices of the Title X project. The regulations, which govern solely the scope of the Title X project's activities, do not in any way restrict the activities of those persons acting as private individuals.

Reacting to the petitioners' argument that the regulations violate a woman's Fifth Amendment right to choose to terminate her pregnancy, Rehnquist wrote, "Congress' refusal to fund abortion counseling and advocacy leaves a pregnant woman with the same choices as if the government had chosen not to fund family-planning services at all."

A Dissenting Opinion

Justice Harry Blackmun expressed one of the core points of disagreement with the majority opinion as he wrote, "Until today, the Court never has upheld viewpoint-based suppression of speech simply because that suppression was a condition upon the acceptance of public funds."

Blackmun, the author of *Roe* v. *Wade* (1973) felt strongly that the ruling in *Rust* lets government interfere with a woman's abortion choice. He agreed with the other dissenters in this case—Justice Thurgood Marshall, Justice John Paul Stevens, and Justice Sandra Day O'Connor—that a strong case could be made that *Rust*, indeed, does violate constitutional rights.

Analyzing the Case

1. What was the wording of the original regulation and how was it expanded?

_____

_____

_____

2. What constitutional objections did the Court reject?

_____

_____

_____

Critical Thinking

3. **Demonstrating Reasoned Judgment** Do you agree that if the federal government funds a program it has the right to control the speech of those participating in that program? Explain your answer.

_____

_____

_____

_____

_____

_____

_____

_____

_____

_____

SUPREME COURT CASE 63

WISCONSIN V. MITCHELL (1992)

Background of the Case

Todd Mitchell, an African American, had been convicted of leading a small group that attacked a white teenaged youth from Kenosha, Wisconsin, in 1989. Before initiating the assault Mitchell had stated, "There goes a white boy, go get him." A jury found that Mitchell had violated the state's hate-crime law. Because of that law, the trial judge increased Mitchell's sentence from the ordinary two years for aggravated battery to four years. A state appeals court upheld the decision. The Wisconsin Supreme Court, however, overruled the hate-crime law as a violation of free speech. It based its decision on the Supreme Court case *R.A.V.* v. *St. Paul*, which stated that legislative bodies could not criminalize biased thought with which it disagreed. Wisconsin then appealed the case to the United States Supreme Court.

More than 20 states and the District of Columbia allowed stiffer sentencing guidelines for bias-motivated crimes. In a seldom seen sign of consensus, 49 states filed a unified brief with the Supreme Court supporting the Wisconsin law.

The case sparked interest and divided opinions around the country. Many civil rights groups supported the Wisconsin law, yet other civil libertarians opposed the statute. For example, the American Civil Liberties Union supported Wisconsin, while the Ohio Chapter of the ACLU filed a brief in support of Mitchell.

Constitutional Issue

The constitutional question to be answered is whether increased penalties for hate-crimes are prohibited by the First and Fourteenth amendments. The First Amendment guarantees freedom of speech. The question here is whether an additional penalty can be levied against someone for a crime that is motivated by a belief. The Fourteenth Amendment allows for "equal protection under the law;" thus the question is whether a person is being treated fairly or unfairly by a court enhancing punishment for bias-motivated crimes.

The Court's Decision

In a unanimous decision, the Supreme Court ruled for the state of Wisconsin and overturned the Wisconsin Supreme Court's decision that the hate-crime statute violated the First Amendment. Chief Justice William H. Rehnquist wrote for the Court.

Rehnquist cited the use of the *R.A.V.* v. *St. Paul* by the Wisconsin Supreme Court. However, he rejected the argument that the case could be applied to a limitless variety of behavior that could be labeled free-speech. Therefore, physical assault could not be protected under the First Amendment. He also went on to say that judges historically have considered many factors in addition to evidence when considering what sentence to enforce on a defendant that is convicted. Thus, the defendant's motive is an important consideration. The Chief Justice also held that a defendant's abstract beliefs, however offensive, should not be taken into account by a sentencing judge.

Mitchell had argued that the enhanced penalty was invalid in that it punished his bias as a motive for the act. Yet, Rehnquist held that motive plays the same role under state and federal anti-discrimination laws, which have previously been upheld under constitutional challenge.

The *R.A.V.* case involved a First Amendment challenge against an ordinance that prohibited "fighting words" from being used that might provoke violence on the basis of race, gender, or religion. The ordinance was held unconstitutional because it was directed at expression (i.e. free-speech). Yet, Mitchell's conduct is unprotected by the First Amendment.

The Wisconsin law enhanced punishment for bias-motivated crime because such crime inflicts greater damage on the individual and society as a whole. For example, bias-motivated crimes are likely to incite retaliatory crimes, thus inflicting greater harm on a community.

Rehnquist concluded that Wisconsin's desire to reduce the harm of bias-motivated crimes on their communities was adequate explanation for the enhancement penalties. Therefore, the law did not violate the First and Fourteenth Amendments.

Analyzing the Case

1. What is a bias-motivated crime?

_____

_____

_____

2. Does the decision in *Wisconsin* v. *Mitchell* mean that judges can take a defendant's beliefs into account when handing out a sentence in any case? Explain.

_____

_____

_____

Critical Thinking

3. **Identifying Central Issues** What is the difference between a law that criminalizes biased thought and a law that allows stiffer penalties for bias-motivated crime?

_____

_____

_____

_____

_____

_____

_____

_____

_____

_____

SUPREME COURT CASE   64

U.S. V. ALVAREZ MACHAIN (1992)

Background of the Case

Humberto Alvarez Machain, a Mexican citizen, was a suspect in the murders of Enrique Camareno, a U.S. Drug Enforcement Administration agent, and a Mexican pilot near Guadalajara, Mexico in 1985. Thus, the United States government attempted to extradite Alvarez to stand trial. However, Mexican authorities refused to release Alvarez to the United States.

The Drug Enforcement Agency (DEA), with the authorization of the executive branch of the United States, hired a bounty hunter to retrieve Alvarez. After being returned to American soil, Alvarez was arrested and set to stand trial. The Mexican government expressed outrage over Alvarez's kidnapping, believing it was a violation of a 1978 extradition treaty between the United States and Mexico. Subsequently, U.S. district and appellate courts dismissed charges against Alvarez on the grounds of the treaty and ordered him to be returned to Mexico.

The United States government appealed the case to the Supreme Court.

Constitutional Issue

The constitutional issue is one of national sovereignty in relationship to treaties and international law. The constitution establishes the sovereignty of the Untied States. Does this sovereignty allow the United States to infringe on the laws of another country? Moreover, does a treaty or international law override the ability of the United States to uphold its laws when suspects flee to foreign countries?

The Court's Decision

In a controversial decision, the Supreme Court ruled 6-3, that the United States was entitled to kidnap criminal suspects from other countries for trial in the United States, regardless of a foreign nation's protests or the terms of an extradition treaty. Therefore, the federal case against Alvarez was reinstated. The Court's decision was written by Chief Justice William H. Rehnquist.

Chief Rehnquist stated that the United States-Mexico extradition treaty did not exclusively prohibit kidnapping. He also explained that principles of international law did not require nations to abide exclusively by an extradition treaty if such an agreement exists between them.

The Court cited *Ker* v. *Illinois*, an 1886 ruling that allowed the abduction of a United States fugitive from Peru as a precedent for its ruling. Ruling in favor of the kidnapping potentially had enormous implications for the United States prosecution of criminals abroad. Extradition treaties existed between the United States and 103 other nations. None of these treaties had exclusive language prohibiting the use of forcible abduction. Therefore, the ruling also appeared to allow other countries the right to abduct criminal suspects from within the United States.

A Dissenting Opinion

Justice John Paul Stevens called the Court's ruling "monstrous" and "shocking" in his dissent with the Court. Stevens believed that the ruling was a violation of the U.S.-Mexican agreement and of international law.

Stevens stated that the Court failed to make a difference between the acts of private citizens, which do not violate international law or extradition treaties, and those authorized by the executive branch of the United States, as in *Alvarez*. He believed that the U.S.-Mexican agreement, while it did not prohibit kidnapping specifically, was meant to cover all possible extraditable offenses. Thus, by claiming that a treaty allows for kidnapping by not exclusively prohibiting it, the decision renders such an agreement practically worthless.

Stevens went on to quote Thomas Paine, whose ideas of liberty influenced the American Revolution. Paine believed that the desire to punish was dangerous to liberty because it leads a nation to stretch, misinterpret, and even misapply laws meant to guarantee freedom. Continuing, Paine believed that a nation must even guard his enemy from oppression, because not doing so establishes a precedent that could reach back to itself.

Analyzing the Case

1. What federal agency arrested Alvarez?

_____

_____

_____

2. How might this decision affect United States relations with other nations?

_____

_____

_____

Critical Thinking

3. **Predicting Consequences** On what grounds did Justice Stevens claim that the decision rendered many international agreements worthless?

_____

_____

_____

_____

_____

_____

_____

_____

_____

_____

_____

SUPREME COURT CASE   65

SHAW V. RENO (1993)

Background of the Case

The case involved North Carolina's 12th Congressional District, which state legislators had redrawn in 1991 to form two African American majority voting districts. Redistricting was done in response to a Justice Department mandate. In the order, the federal government had directed the state to comply with the Voting Rights Act, passed in 1965 and amended in 1982 to increase minority political representation. In the 1992 election, the 12th District elected Melvin Watt to the House of Representatives. Mr. Watt and Eva Clayton, who was elected from the other minority district, were the first African Americans to represent North Carolina since 1901.

Five white North Carolinians sued the state and federal government over the design of the 12th District. The district spanned 160 miles in a snake-like pattern to include exclusively African American neighborhoods along Interstate 85. They argued that the white population's Constitutional rights had been violated under the redistricting.

The case had significant implications because there were 50 electoral districts that had been redrawn in the United States to form minority districts. Twenty-six of the districts were created for the 1992 election. Redistricting flowed from the 1990 census and federal mandates to increase minority participation.

Constitutional Question

The case hinges on the Fourteenth Amendment's "equal protection under the law." Those filing the suit believed the way the 12th District was redistricted violated their right to equal protection under the law. The defendants held that whites had a majority of the districts, thus they were more than equally protected.

The Court's Decision

The Supreme Court ruled in a 5-4 decision that states with irregularly shaped electoral districts, drawn for the intent of creating minority districts, could be challenged constitutionally. Justice Sandra Day O'Connor writing for the Court stated that the "bizarre" shaped district resembled the "most egregious racial gerrymanders of the past" which had excluded African Americans.

Justice O'Connor stated there are legitimate reasons for states to provide minority districts. She believed, however, that "traditional districting principles" in regard to compactness, contiguity, and other political divisions must be respected. The justice drew a comparison between linking a geographical area together strictly on the basis of skin color to that of a "political apartheid."

The majority opinion went on to say that there must be "compelling state interest" for officials to distinguish treatment on the basis of race. Furthermore, citing the Voting Rights Act by itself was insufficient as proof of such interest. O'Connor said that a state's duty to follow antidiscrimination laws does not allow it to engage in "racial gerrymandering."

A Dissenting Opinion

The dissenting justices believed that white voters had not been harmed by the redrawing of the 12th District. The dissent also criticized the emphasis on the shape of the district. They believed discriminatory gerrymandering could take place in a regularly shaped district as easily as in an odd-shaped district.

Justice John Paul Stevens stated that the duty to govern impartially is abused when the group with power over the election process defines electoral boundaries to enhance its own political strength at the expense of minorities. However, the duty to be impartial is not violated when the majority tries to facilitate the election of a member from the minority.

Justice David Souter held that legislators have to take race into account when drawing district lines, in order to avoid the dilution of the minority vote. Continuing, Souter believed that if redistricting harms participation in the election process, then the Fourteenth Amendment is violated. He held that because no one's participation had been harmed the redrawing of the 12th District did not violate the Fourteenth Amendment.

Analyzing the Case

1. What was the purpose of the redrawing of District 12 that led to the court case?

_____

_____

_____

2. On what constitutional principle were those who brought the case to court relying?

_____

_____

_____

Critical Thinking

3. Making Inferences Did the decision in this case mean that in the future states could not redraw legislative districts to increase minority representation?

_____

_____

_____

_____

_____

_____

_____

_____

_____

_____

_____

SUPREME COURT CASE 66

NATIONAL ORGANIZATION FOR WOMEN (NOW) V. SCHEIDLER (1994)

Background of the Case

The National Organization for Women (NOW), which supports a woman's right to an abortion, filed a lawsuit against individuals and groups for their antiabortion activity. NOW claimed that these individuals and groups had used violent and criminal tactics in their protests. The defendants included Joseph Scheidler, who led the Pro-Life Action League; Randall Terry, leader of Operation Rescue; the Pro-Life Direct Action League; and Project Life. Activists belonging to these groups had been charged with robbing, defacing, and throwing fire bombs at abortion clinics, and with having threatened abortion doctors.

The main issue in the case was whether the pro-life individuals and groups could be held liable under the Racketeer Influenced and Corrupt Organizations Act (RICO). RICO made it illegal for groups to use violence or extortion in an attempt to close down businesses or organizations. Targeting organized crime in 1970 when it was enacted by Congress, the law made it illegal for an "enterprise" to undertake a "pattern of racketeering." Proof of two or more criminal acts constituted a pattern.

Those found guilty under RICO were responsible for three times the damages caused. The threat of triple damages was meant to be a strong deterrent against violent activity. However, pro-life activists stated their plan to continue demonstrating, and expressed faith that they could defeat the lawsuit.

A federal district court dismissed NOW's case in 1991. It stated the language used in RICO required "an economic motive." The prosecution had not proved that an individual or group accused of racketeering had "some profit-generating purpose." The 7th U.S. Court of Appeals upheld the district court's ruling and the case was appealed to the Supreme Court.

The case had taken on additional importance because the Supreme Court had ruled earlier in January of 1993 that courts could not use civil-rights laws to stop antiabortion protests. The Clinton administration filed a brief in support of NOW, in part due to a desire to use RICO against terrorists who might not be motivated by monetary gain.

Constitutional Issue

The constitutional question to be answered was whether the RICO law as applied to antiabortion activity violated First Amendment rights. The defendants felt that their "freedom of speech" was being challenged by trying to apply a racketeering law to the expression of their beliefs.

The Court's Decision

On January 24, 1994, the Supreme Court ruled unanimously that abortion-rights groups could use the RICO law. Pro-choice groups could sue antiabortion groups and demonstrators who had supposedly organized violent and criminal acts against abortion clinics and abortion doctors. Chief Justice Rehnquist wrote for the Court.

Rehnquist stated that RICO could certainly be used in the case, even if the group involved did not have any financial motive. He went on to say that "the fact RICO has been applied in situations not expressly anticipated by Congress does not demonstrate ambiguity." The Chief Justice felt the law was not ambiguous but that it was capable of handling a wide variety of cases.

Rehnquist also wrote that the case did not involve a First Amendment issue in regard to "free-speech," because violent and criminal activity are not protected under the First Amendment. In a concurring opinion, however, Justices Souter and Kennedy expressed a note of caution. Though they felt the *Scheidler* case involving RICO did not violate the First Amendment, they urged courts applying RICO to use prudence due to the "First Amendment interests that could be at stake." The Court's decision allowed NOW to refile its lawsuit in a trial court in Chicago.

Analyzing the Case

1. What was the original intent of the RICO Act?

_____

_____

_____

2. What requirement did the federal district court say the prosecution had not met for including antiabortion demonstrators under RICO?

_____

_____

_____

Critical Thinking

3. **Demonstrating Reasoned Judgment** Congress had not anticipated that the RICO law could be used against individuals or groups other than organized crime. Do you believe that the Supreme Court should have the power to apply laws in ways other than those originally intended? Explain.

_____

_____

_____

_____

_____

_____

_____

_____

_____

_____

_____

1 *Marbury* v. *Madison*

1. For any right, a corresponding remedy for any violation of that right must exist.

2. The Court has no authority over a cabinet officer in the officer's political role, only over actions as directed by law; the law providing such authority was unconstitutional.

3. It established the principle of judicial review. By establishing the principle of judicial review, *Marbury* provides a check on the laws passed by Congress and signed by the President.

4. Answers will vary, but students should support their opinions.

2 *McCulloch* v. *Maryland*

1. Implied powers are those not specifically stated in the Constitution but that allow Congress to take whatever action is necessary to carry out its specified duties.

2. It gives Congress the authority to make laws required to carry out its assigned tasks.

3. The Bank was immune because it was an institution of the federal government. The federal government is not a subject of any state, and such a tax would impose an indirect tax on citizens in other states. In a federal-state conflict, the state must yield. Furthermore, the power to tax is the power to destroy; therefore Congress had a right to take necessary steps to preserve an institution it had created.

4. Answers should indicate that the ruling clearly made the federal government supreme.

3 *Gibbons* v. *Ogden*

1. Ogden operated under a monopoly grant originally issued by New York State. Gibbons held a federal coasting trade license.

2. Congress gets its power to regulate commerce within a state by following commerce from one state into another state.

3. It left the question open for the time being.

4 *Dred Scott* v. *Sanford*

1. Slavery had been forbidden in the territory according to terms of the Missouri Compromise of 1820.

2. Being a state citizen did not automatically mean a person was also a citizen of the United States. Only Congress had the right to grant national citizenship.

3. A territory, upon achieving statehood, had all powers guaranteed states by the Constitution. Slavery was authorized by the Constitution, according to Taney, and Congress, therefore, could not alter a person's right to own slaves or any other kind of property. Answers may vary regarding the relationship between the Missouri Compromise and citizenship for Dred Scott. Students should mention that the manner in which the compromise was interpreted determined Scott's status. This reflected continuing clashes between states' rights advocates and strict constructionists.

5 *Ex Parte Milligan*

1. Davis concluded that the use of military authority was not granted by Congress to try civilians, especially if civilian courts were still functioning.

2. The military infringed on Milligan's rights by arresting and trying him in a military court that did not have power to try civilians and was not a court established by Congress.

3. Answers will vary, but the example would have to describe a crisis in which the civil court system was not operating.

6 *Reynolds* v. *United States*

1. Congress had the right to legislate practices that might have a harmful effect on the social order. In this case, polygamy was not viewed as part of a religious belief but as harmful practice. Congress, therefore, had the right to prohibit such practice.

2. Because polygamy had been outlawed or prohibited, the Court did not believe that the First Amendment's intent was to make it permissible.

3. The decision determined that the freedom of religion has its limitations as do other freedoms guaranteed by the Constitution.

4. Answers will vary, but should indicate that total "freedom" may lead to anarchy.

7 *Plessy* v. *Ferguson*

1. Plessy appealed on the grounds that Louisiana's law violated the Thirteenth Amendment.

2. Brown labeled as fallacy the idea that separation necessarily implies inferiority of either race.

3. The Fourteenth Amendment guarantees racial equality in legal, but not in social, matters. Therefore, a state may provide separate but equal facilities.

4. Harlan saw racial segregation as "wholly inconsistent" with the principles of personal freedom and equality before the law was guaranteed by the Constitution.

8 *Weeks* v. *United States*

1. A warrant must describe the specific persons and places to be searched or seized.

2. It applied only to federal officials and courts, not to the states.

3. Common law held that illegally obtained evidence was admissible in a trial. In the *Weeks* case, the Court ruling applied only to federal officials involved, not to police.

9 *Gitlow* v. *New York*

1. Criminal anarchy is the doctrine that organized government should be violently overthrown and its leaders assassinated.

2. The Court did not defend the application of First Amendment protections to the states; rather, it assumed the application of these rights to the states under the Fourteenth Amendment's due process clause.

3. No; the Court held that the entire class of subversive speech could be constitutionally prohibited. It was not necessary to prove that such speech would produce a specific result.

4. Answers will vary, but students should support their answers.

10 *Olmstead* v. *United States*

1. The Eighteenth Amendment outlawed the import, manufacture, and sale of alcoholic beverages.

2. The Court held that the Fourth Amendment was not applicable because there was no evidence of physical entry and nothing was seized.

3. Taft feared that society would suffer on account of the immunity criminals would receive. Answers will vary.

11 *Near* v. *Minnesota*

1. Examples are in times of war or against obscene publications.

2. The primary purpose is to prevent prior restraint on publication.

3. A person can sue under the laws governing libel, but may not prevent the material from being published in the first place.

12 *Powell* v. *Alabama*

1. A capital case involves a crime punishable by death.

2. The precedent was that certain rights mentioned in the Bill of Rights must also be included in the concept of due process and its interpretation.

3. The defendants were given too speedy a trial, with no time to prepare their defense with a lawyer.

4. Racial prejudice would be a major factor in those days. Answers will vary.

13 *De Jonge* v. *Oregon*

1. Criminal syndicalism is the doctrine that violence may be used to affect political change or revolution.

2. The right to assemble peaceably is part of the foundation of United States civil and political institutions in much the same way as are free press and free speech.

3. For the first time, the Court held that the Fourteenth Amendment includes the right of assembly under the due process clause.

4. Answers will vary, but students may describe situations that touch on other Court decisions, such as when a speaker at an assembly incites disorderly conduct or riot.

14 *Minersville School District* v. *Gobitis*

1. Gobitis claimed that because his children had been expelled from public schools and school attendance was compulsory, he was forced to place them in private schools.

2. The flag salute helped form a sense of patriotism, or "cohesive sentiment," which is at the basis of a free society.

3. The Court said it was not competent to overrule the wisdom of the legislature and that it was not up to the courts to decide on issues of educational policy.

4. Answers will vary, but students should support their opinions.

15 *Betts* v. *Brady*

1. Earlier law (e.g., common, colonial, and prior state laws) could be interpreted as allowing, but not requiring, that a defendant be represented by counsel.

2. The Sixth Amendment places limitations on Congress. Matters related to the state must be viewed in light of the due process clause of the Fourteenth Amendment.

3. Black felt that the right to counsel was fundamental to a fair trial and that the states must provide this as an obligation under the Fourteenth Amendment.

4. Roberts maintains that the guarantee is rooted in the power of any judge to appoint counsel if required. Student opinions will vary.

16 West Virginia State Board of Education v. Barnette

1. The flag salute was considered a form of speech.

2. The main purpose of the Bill of Rights is to remove certain subjects from political vicissitudes and control by majorities and officials, and to establish them as legal principles to be applied by the courts.

3. Essentially, state regulation can occur only to prevent grave and immediate danger. Answers will vary.

17 Korematsu v. United States

1. The evacuation orders were based on the war powers of the President and Congress.

2. Murphy argued that the Japanese Americans had been deprived of equal protection of the law and procedural due process under the Fifth Amendment.

3. Jackson was concerned that the Court's decision would serve as a precedent and become "the doctrine of the Constitution." Answers will vary.

18 Everson v. Board of Education

1. His tax money was being used to pay transportation costs for children attending private and parochial schools.

2. Justice Rutledge argued that the cost of transportation was part of the cost of education, and since the instruction was primarily religious, reimbursement for transportation costs was not allowable.

3. Justice Black stated that in using tax money for public transportation, the state was not contributing money directly to the schools but providing a general program, available to the public as a whole, to help parents get their children to and from accredited schools.

19 McCollum v. Board of Education

1. The employer was the Champaign Council on Religious Education.

2. The state used tax-supported facilities to help spread religious faith.

3. Each should remain separate and free from the other.

4. Answers will vary, but students should support their opinions.

20 Dennis v. United States

1. The Smith Act made it illegal to teach or advocate the violent overthrow of the United States government.

2. The Court held that the government had the power to protect itself against rebellion; this power being a basic constitutional principle.

3. Answers will vary, but students should support their opinions.

21 Feiner v. New York

1. Irving Feiner was charged with disorderly conduct.

2. The Cantwell decision stated that, in order to control an immediate threat to public order or safety when there is clear and present danger, the state (i.e., police) may intervene.

3. Answers will vary, but students should support their opinions.

22 Brown v. Board of Education of Topeka, Kansas

1. In Sweatt, no separate but equal school facility was available.

2. Do separate but equal public facilities violate the Fourteenth Amendment's guarantee of equal protection of the law?

3. The Court evaluated the effect of segregated schools on African American pupils. As a result, it ruled that separate could not be equal.

4. Answers will vary, but students should support their opinions.

23 Yates v. United States

1. Advocacy is the abstract expression of principles; incitement is the encouragement of action based on those principles.

2. The trial judge thought it was necessary only to prove advocacy, not incitement.

3. Schenck held that the First Amendment could be set aside in cases of "clear and present danger." Dennis changed the standard to "clear and probable." The Yates case was understood to have signalled a return to the "clear and present danger" ruling of the Schenck case.

24 Mapp v. Ohio

1. It is implied from the Fourth Amendment's prohibition against unreasonable search and seizure.

2. The Fourth Amendment can be applied to the states through the due process clause of the Fourteenth Amendment.

3. Prior to Mapp, evidence rejected as illegally obtained in a federal court could still be used in state courts.

4. Answers will vary, but students should support their opinions.

25 *Baker* v. *Carr*

1. Nonjusticiable political questions include those related to Native American nations, foreign relations, and matters that would overstep the bounds of the separation of powers.

2. The guaranty clause of Article 4, Section 4, of the Constitution guarantees a republican form of government to each state.

3. The Court held that since there is no improper political question for the judiciary to decide, the case could be heard under the judicially manageable standards of the Fourteenth Amendment's equal protection clause.

26 *Engel* v. *Vitale*

1. The First Amendment prohibits laws respecting either the free exercise or the establishment of religion.

2. Vitale said the prayer was nondenominational and no one was compelled to say it or listen to it.

3. Black recalled that the colonists had come to America from England to escape governmental interference in religion or religious matters.

4. Answers will vary, but students should understand that the Founders were not against religion per se, but wanted to keep government out of direct involvement in the support of any religion or religious practices.

27 *Abington School District* v. *Schempp*

1. No; the Bible could be studied as history or literature.

2. The government must take a position of strict neutrality; it can neither advance nor inhibit religion.

3. Both states maintained that readings served secular, moral, and educational purposes.

28 *Gideon* v. *Wainwright*

1. Gideon submitted an *in forma pauperis* petition; such a device is available to a person unable to afford the hiring of a lawyer to petition for him.

2. No; the Court kept the "fundamental and essential" standard found in *Betts* but now applied it to the right of counsel in all criminal cases.

3. Black thought that even an intelligent layman, or average citizen, lacked expertise and knowledge of legal procedures and processes.

4. Black felt that if governments and people of wealth spend large amounts on counsel, it is obvious that counsel is necessary. Accepting that, it is unfair for the poor to have to defend themselves.

29 *Escobedo* v. *Illinois*

1. Legal counsel must be provided when the process of investigation shifts to accusation and the police are seeking a confession.

2. The accused has the right to be advised of the constitutional protection against self-incrimination.

3. Answers will vary, but reference should be made in either instance to the balance struck by the Constitution in favor of the accused.

4. Answers will vary, but students should support their opinions.

30 *Reynolds* v. *Sims*

1. The Court had to decide whether both houses of a bicameral legislature had to reflect equal numbers of people in a voting district.

2. The votes in one area would make those in the smaller areas ineffective.

3. The Court rejected the argument that used the analogy of the U.S. Senate, making states and counties analogous. Unlike states, counties are not independent entities.

4. Answers will vary, but should include the importance of every person's vote being equal in a democracy.

31 *Wesberry* v. *Sanders*

1. Wesberry's district had two to three times the population of other voting districts in Georgia, which meant that his vote was worth less than those of some other voters.

2. According to Black, it means that all votes must be substantially equal. Representation must reflect population.

3. Harlan argued that population is not the only factor intended by the Constitution to count in voting district apportionment. He said, too, that the Court was intruding on the exclusive supervisory power of Congress.

4. Answers will vary, but students should support their opinions.

32 *Miranda* v. *Arizona*

1. No person can be compelled to be a witness against himself or herself in a criminal case.

2. Custodial interrogation refers to any questioning by law enforcement officials that takes place once a suspect has been arrested or deprived of freedom to some significant degree.

3. The *Miranda* decision allows questioning that occurs at the scene of the crime or in order to establish facts as opposed to guilt.

4. Answers will vary, but students should support their opinions.

33 *Sheppard* v. *Maxwell*

1. It is an order to bring a prisoner before a judge to determine whether due process has been violated.

2. The trial judge failed to protect Sheppard from the effects of prejudicial publicity before and during the trial.

3. Answers will vary, but may include: the judge could have prevented various officials and others from giving statements to the press; the judge could have warned the press about what could and could not be published or broadcast; the jurors could have been properly sequestered and kept from telephones or reading newspapers.

34 *In re Gault*

1. Gerald Gault was denied: 1) the right to receive notice of charges against him; 2) the right to counsel; 3) the right to confrontation and cross-examination; 4) privilege against self-incrimination; 5) the right to a transcript of proceedings; and 6) the right to appellate review.

2. Gerald's accuser was not present at the hearings, no records of the proceedings were made, and not enough time was allowed to him prior to each hearing.

3. Answers will vary, but students should support their opinions.

35 *Katz* v. *United States*

1. The FBI claimed that their surveillance was legal because their wiretap was on the outside of the telephone booth, which was not a "constitutionally protected area."

2. Katz and the government based their argument on the physical placement of the wiretap; the Court held that the Fourth Amendment protects people, not places.

3. Yes; recording Katz's conversations would have been legal if a warrant had been obtained in advance.

36 *Gregory* v. *Chicago*

1. The Illinois Supreme Court said the demonstrators were arrested more for disobeying police orders to disperse than for marching.

2. No evidence existed that the marchers had been disorderly; therefore they were protected by the First Amendment.

3. Black's objection to the statute was that it was "unconstitutionally vague."

4. Warren's conclusions were based on the conduct of the marchers. Black's conclusions were based on the weakness of the statute.

37 *Tinker* v. *Des Moines School District*

1. The interests of the school authorities in orderly conduct and of the students' rights to freedom of expression were in conflict.

2. The right of free expression is not absolute in the sense that it must not disrupt classes or interfere with the rights of other students.

3. At all times and places a person has fundamental rights and protections under the Constitution.

38 *New York Times Co.* v. *United States*

1. The Court ruled that the government had not proved the necessity of prior restraint on publication of "The Pentagon Papers."

2. Douglas noted that Congress had specifically rejected a law that would have authorized the government to prevent publication of certain materials during a national emergency.

3. Answers will vary, but should include the fact that there was a question of possibly endangering national security.

39 *Miller* v. *California*

1. a.) Does a work, when viewed as a whole, appeal to an individual's prurient interest? b.) Does the work show sexually explicit acts in a patently offensive way? c.) Is there a lack of serious literary, artistic, political, or scientific value?

2. The principles of the First Amendment apply exactly the same in every state. Material considered permissible under First Amendment principles in one state, however, may not be so considered in another state.

3. Douglas was mainly concerned that the standard for "obscenity" was too vague and that only a constitutional amendment could define it.

4. Answers will vary, but should include the idea that if persons publish irresponsibly and harm others, society must have legal recourse.

40 *Roe* v. *Wade*

1. It stems from the Bill of Rights in general and the Fourteenth Amendment's guarantee of liberty.

2. The dual interest is protecting the health of the mother and protecting the potential of human life.

3. The point is until the end of the first trimester, or three-month period, of pregnancy.

41 *Lau* v. *Nichols*

1. None; the case was decided on the basis of the 1964 Civil Rights Act.

2. The mockery was the requirement that a child already have a skill that the program was supposed to teach him or her.

3. Answers will vary, but should include the idea that drawing the line as to the number of children required for a program to be put into place, could be difficult.

42 *United States* v. *Nixon*

1. Executive privilege might have been properly asserted if it was necessary to protect military, diplomatic, or national security plans or secrets.

2. The reasons were the need to protect the confidentiality of high-level communications and to maintain the independence of the Executive Branch through the separation of powers.

3. Opposed to the President's claim were the importance of the subpoena in enforcing criminal statutes and the rights of the accused guaranteed by the Fifth and Sixth Amendments.

43 *Gregg* v. *Georgia*

1. One example would be a person's previous criminal record.

2. The Court would presume its validity because the death penalty had been selected by a democratically chosen legislature.

3. Retribution by a state may prevent people from carrying out punishment themselves, as, for example, in the case of vigilantes. Answers will vary, but students should support their opinions.

44 *Washington* v. *Davis*

1. Four times as many African Americans as whites failed the test.

2. A racially discriminatory purpose was not proved.

3. The case was decided primarily on the equal protection clause of the Fourteenth Amendment.

4. Answers will vary, but students might mention standardized school exams that appear to put African Americans and other minority groups at a disadvantage.

45 *Regents of the University of California* v. *Bakke*

1. No; the Amendment is framed in universal terms.

2. Bakke personally had no responsibility for the harm that any racial or ethnic group had suffered.

3. The Court said that when racial considerations were the only criterion, it must be shown that such a classification is necessary.

46 *Kaiser Aluminum and Chemical Corporation (and United Steelworkers of America)* v. *Weber*

1. The Court interpreted the true purpose of Title VII as designed to break down old patterns of discrimination against African Americans and to open up job opportunities previously closed to them.

2. A literal reading did not contain the spirit or intention of the law.

3. Answers will vary, but students may feel that the Kaiser plan discriminated against employees who were not African Americans.

47 *Rostker* v. *Goldberg*

1. The constitutional basis was the due process clause of the Fifth Amendment.

2. These points were: 1) Congress considered the issue at length and not in light of "a traditional way of thinking about women"; and 2) women as a group were not eligible for combat.

3. Marshall expressed concern that women excluded from the draft are also excluded from a "fundamental civic obligation."

4. Answers will vary, but students should support their opinions.

48 *Immigration and Naturalization Service* v. *Chadha*

1. Chadha's case was based on the claim that the one-House legislative veto provision was unconstitutional under Article I of the Constitution.

2. It was unconstitutional because, as a legislative act, it required passage by both Houses and presentation to the President.

3. Answers will vary, but students should support their opinions.

49 *New Jersey* v. *T.L.O.*

1. She was caught smoking by a teacher but denied it; the vice principal was looking for evidence that she had been smoking.

2. Answers will vary, but students should support their opinions.

3. Obtain a search warrant and show "probable cause" for the search.

4. The need for school officials to maintain order and discipline justified slightly restricting students' rights under the Fourth Amendment.

50 *Wallace* v. *Jaffree*

1. A law that requires a short period of time in the school day, a moment-of-silence, to be set aside for meditation.

2. The Court found that the clear intent of the Alabama Legislature was to use the law to promote prayer in school.

3. Black thought it was meaningless or even hostile to religion for the Court to distinguish between moment-of-silence laws that included the word "prayer" and those that did not.

51 *Bethel School District* v. *Fraser*

1. Fraser's obscene speech in the assembly violated the school's disruptive conduct rule.

2. The responsibility to prepare citizens who would behave in socially acceptable ways could require school officials to put certain limits on students' speech in school.

3. *Tinker* set the precedent that students do not lose their constitutional rights to free speech at "the schoolhouse gate."

4. The speech in the *Fraser* case, unlike *Tinker*, was (1) not essentially political, and (2) disruptive of the school's educational mission.

52 *South Dakota* v. *Dole*

1. The case was based on the claim that the federal law violated constitutional limits on the spending power of Congress under Article I and that it also violates the Twenty-first Amendment.

2. Congress did have the constitutional right to "purchase," but not "coerce" the states' compliance with the law.

3. Answers will vary, but students should support their opinions.

53 *Hazelwood School District* v. *Kuhlmeier*

1. A story on student pregnancy and one on divorce.

2. The school paper was part of the school curriculum rather than a public forum and, as a result, under the control of the school officials.

3. Answers will vary, but students should support their opinions.

54 *Skinner* v. *Railway Labor Executives Association*

1. The Court ruled to allow the drug testing because the compelling government interest in decreasing the number of train fatalities due to drug-related accidents was judged more important than employees' privacy.

2. Marshall felt that the Court was wrong to react to a momentary emergency at the expense of Fourth Amendment rights.

3. Answers will vary, but students should support their opinions.

55 *Cruzan* v. *Director, Missouri Department of Health*

1. The State Supreme Court ruled that its State Living Will statute expressed a strong policy favoring preservation of life and said that Nancy's statements to her former housemate were unreliable.

2. A Living Will document that Nancy Cruzan had signed would be such evidence.

3. Answers will vary, but students should support their opinions.

56 *Michigan Department of State Police* v. *Sitz*

1. Rehnquist felt that the seizure was reasonable when the need to reduce drunken driving was weighed against the intrusion on motorists.

2. Stevens felt that the subjective intrusion on motorists was substantial and unreasonable; Rehnquist felt that it was reasonable.

3. Answers will vary, but students should support their opinions.

57 *Board of Education of Oklahoma Public Schools* v. *Dowell*

1. The federal court order called for 1) mandatory student assignments for many schools and grades; and 2) school busing.

2. The constitutional basis for their case was the equal protection clause of the Fourteenth Amendment.

3. Marshall felt that there was still need of the federal decree because its goals and purposes had, in fact, not been achieved.

58 *California* v. *Acevedo*

1. The constitutional basis of the case was the Fourth Amendment rights that protect against unreasonable search and seizure.

2. Blackmun felt that as long as there was probable cause, a search could proceed without a warrant; Stevens argued for a stricter interpretation of the Fourth Amendment and the need for a warrant.

3. Answers will vary, but students should support their opinions.

59 *International Union UAW* v. *Johnson Controls, Inc.*

1. Women were being barred from lead-exposed jobs because lead exposure can harm an unborn fetus.

2. The Civil Rights Act of 1964 prohibits sex-based classifications related to all phases of employment.

3. White expressed concern that companies should be able to protect themselves against possible future lawsuits due to prenatal injury. Answers will vary, but students should support their opinions.

60 *Arizona* v. *Fulminante*

1. The trial court ruled that the confessions were allowable; the Arizona Supreme Court ruled that a retrial should take place without the use of the first confession.

2. The constitutional basis was possible violation of rights under the Fifth and Fourteenth Amendments.

3. Now, a coerced confession does not necessarily reverse a conviction.

4. Answers will vary, but students should support their opinions.

61 *County of Riverside* v. *McLaughlin*

1. McLaughlin claimed that he had been denied his Fourth Amendment right to a speedy trial.

2. Delays for gathering additional evidence to support the arrest, those motivated by ill will against the defendant, and delay for delay's sake.

3. Answers will vary, but students should support their opinions.

62 *Rust* v. *Sullivan*

1. The original regulation stated that no federal funds could be used to support federally funded family planning clinics having "programs where abortion is a method of family planning." It was expanded to include counseling about abortion.

2. The Court rejected the claims that the regulation violated First Amendment free speech rights and Fifth Amendment rights of a woman to choose to terminate a pregnancy.

3. Answers will vary, but students should support their opinions.

63 *Wisconsin* v. *Mitchell*

1. A crime in which bias against a person's race, religion, or gender plays a role.

2. No. The Court said that a defendant's abstract beliefs should not be taken into account by a sentencing judge.

3. A law that criminalizes biased thought violates a person's freedom of speech. Allowing stiffer penalties for bias-motivated crime does not punish a person for their bias alone. That bias must be shown to have played a role in a criminal activity.

64 *U.S.* v. *Alvarez Machain*

1. Drug Enforcement Agency

2. It appeared to permit other nations to abduct American citizens within the United States for trial abroad.

3. Any agreement that does not specifically prohibit abductions or any other act may be rendered worthless by a high court decision.

65 *Shaw* v. *Reno*

1. To increase minority political representation.

2. "equal protection of the law" in the Fourteenth Amendment

3. No. States could do so if they avoided breaking the rules of contiguity and compactness.

66 *NOW* v. *Scheidler*

1. To make it illegal for organized criminals to use violence or extortion to shut down businesses.

2. The court required the prosecution to show an economic motive or profit-generating purpose on the part of the defendants.

3. Answers will vary, but students should consider the power of judicial review.